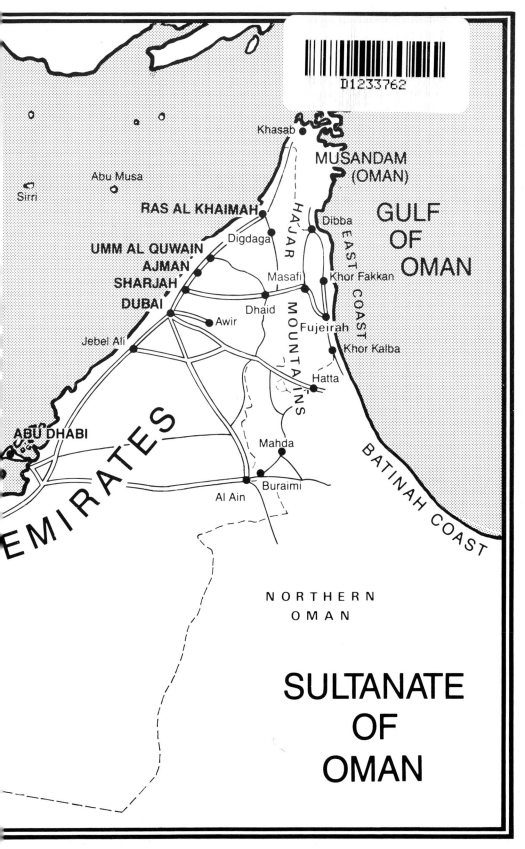

The **BIRDS** of the
United Arab Emirates

BRITISH BIRDS, Vol. 89, No. 5, May 1996, p. 219 + (incl photos)
'the United Arab Emirates', Colin Richardson

The
BIRDS
of the
United Arab Emirates

by Colin Richardson

drawings by Bill Morton and Margaret Henderson

Foreword by Michael Gallagher

With kind support from the Hatta Fort Hotel, Dubai

Hobby Publications Dubai & Warrington

To Kat, whose patience and good behaviour was finally rewarded.

British Library Cataloguing in Publication Data
Richardson, Colin
   The birds of the United Arab Emirates.
   1. United Arab Emirates. Birds
   I. Title
   598.295357

   ISBN 1-872839-00-2

Printed and bound by Printfine Ltd., Liverpool
First published 1990 by Hobby Publications, 11 Walton Heath Road, Warrington, Cheshire WA4 6HZ, United Kingdom.

CONTENTS

LIST OF PLATES

FOREWORD By Michael Gallagher

The United Arab Emirates is one of the most exciting of Arabia's 'bird frontiers', where millions of birds of hundreds of species come twice a year on migration to and from Asia, Europe and even the sub-Antarctic, where species 'new' to Arabia may still be found, and where a considerable desert fauna is resident.

This has not always been apparent, for the presently known status of the birds, so well described in this book, owes much to the spread of large man-made habitats, well illustrated and identified here, such as irrigated parks, cultivations and even the equally important waste-disposal sites. The ardent and the occasional observer of birds now have excellent opportunities to see many species that were once rarely glimpsed or that passed quickly and unseen.

Colin Richardson's interest, commitment and knowledge gained painstakingly in the field over many years, shows on every page of this lucidly written guide, and have enabled him to give us an enthralling illustrated account of the country and of the species known to occur in the UAE. By equally deep research into the literature he has not neglected those who discovered birds in the Gulf at the turn of the Century, when all was desert and travel was a prolonged adventure. Typically, he gives credit also to fellow observers and gives every encouragement to those who follow.

This book courageously and most successfully breaks new ground. By resisting the temptation to copy the style of the coloured field guides (now readily available) he and his talented team have made it a notable companion to them, with space well-devoted to what those guides do not show or tell us and we need to know: *what* are the birds we are likely to see in UAE, *when* they may be expected, and *where* are the best places to see them. This excellent book will surely encourage even more of us to get out and about, to enjoy the country and our hobby, and to make more discoveries.

Michael Gallagher.

INTRODUCTION

This book is intended as a guide to the birds of the United Arab Emirates and brings together many years of documented records by hundreds of observers. The status and distribution of each species is detailed, many for the first time, accompanied by a timings chart and a breeding map where appropriate. The maps include those parts of Oman adjacent to the Emirates' borders, particularly the Musandam Peninsula which is totally surrounded by UAE territory. With vagrants or very scarce migrants there is often reference to their status in Oman, for comparison in this neighbouring state. Most of the text was completed by December 1989, although some recent information on spring sightings 1990 has been included.

360 species are detailed in the main list, of which 321 are migrants, and 67 species breed regularly. There is also an additional list of 35 species which do not qualify for inclusion on the main list. Many of these are potential species or those which have been reported with insufficient detail for inclusion on the main list. Added to these are ten introduced species, for which there are only isolated nesting reports (e.g. Red-whiskered Bulbul, Rüppell's Weaver, Red Avadavat, Pied and Brahminy Mynahs) but few other sightings, or they are the result of larger scale introduction (such as Egyptian Goose and Black Francolin) which may eventually colonise wider areas. (see 'Exotic introductions on page 12).

For the adventurous birdwatcher the United Arab Emirates lies in a relatively unexplored region, where rare Asian migrants occur and where isolated pockets of elusive residents can be found with a little determination. Birdwatching in the Emirates is often a challenge, but always rewarding.

I have hardly dealt with field identification in the text, except where interesting or distinctive sub-species occur. The photographs show many of the commoner species and form a useful identification aid for the less experienced observer. There are many field guides available and the following are highly recommended: *The Birds of Oman* (Gallagher & Woodcock 1980), *The Birds of Britain and Europe with North Africa and the Middle East* (Fitter, Parslow and Heinzel 1972) and *Birds of the Middle East and North Africa* (Hollom, Porter, Christensen & Willis 1988). Other references are listed on page 172.

Further news and information on local birdwatching can be obtained through natural history groups in Dubai and Abu Dhabi as follows:

Dubai Natural History Group. P.O. Box 9234, Dubai, United Arab Emirates.

Emirates Natural History Group. P.O. Box 2380, Abu Dhabi, United Arab Emirates.

The Drawings

Most regularly occurring species in the systematic list are accompanied by an original line drawing by artist Bill Morton. Although primarily intended as a 'vignette,' all have been carefully researched to portray the race and plumage most likely to be encountered in the field in the UAE.

The cover paintings and site sketches are by Dubai-based artist Margaret Henderson.

The Photographs

Obtaining photographs was not easy. Relatively few photographers have taken UAE birdlife as a serious subject, despite the ideal lighting conditions available.

The photos show species in their typical Emirates' habitat, and in typical plumage. Except in spring few migrants occur in fine breeding dress in Arabia, as portrayed in the field guides, and I felt it would be helpful to feature the more typical immature, wintering and eclipse plumages more likely to be encountered.

I am grateful for all the help and support I received from Mike West and Dave Robinson, who allowed me complete access to their slides, all of which were taken locally in the period between 1982 and 1990. Christian Gross also provided a number of photographs he (and Kevin Hyland) had taken during wildlife research in the remote desert areas of the UAE. Adrian Chapman provided other photographs at the eleventh hour.

The Site Guides

Good birding sites seem to be springing up all over Arabia and particularly in the Emirates as it continually expands its landscape projects. Many of the best sites are in man-made parkland, which depends entirely on continual irrigation for survival. Other sites are near sewage works, water treatment plants and rubbish dumps. All are dependant on Man's influence and can quickly disappear as local priorities change. Opportunities must be taken by birds and birdwatchers alike when the attraction is there.

I have detailed more than 20 of the best 'birding' sites in the 'Where to watch' chapter, but there are doubtless many other places still undiscovered, particularly in the more remote desert and mountain areas. I would be pleased to hear of any new and interesting places.

Some of these locations are in sensitive or restricted areas, particularly the Zabeel Water Treatment Plant and Khor Dubai, both of which are regularly patrolled by police, who may ask you to leave. The (old) Dubai sewage works may be entered easily, but permission should be sought at the administration office near the main entrance. The Emirates Golf Club is for the use of members only and you should introduce yourself to the management when making a trip there. The sites at Jebel Ali and Hatta Fort Hotels both involve exploring the hotel gardens and a birding visit should be undertaken with care and respect. There is often great interest shown by others in your birdwatching activities, and even in such private areas, you are more likely to find much help and hospitality.

The Breeding Maps

There is a breeding map for each species nesting in the United Arab Emirates and the Musandam Peninsula (Oman). The main breeding areas are shown in solid red, with the lighter shading indicating sparser distribution. There is still much to be learnt about the breeding distribution of the UAE's birds, and extent of the range shown on some of the maps is assumed, based on nearby nesting evidence. In some cases a question mark indicates where further study is needed to establish breeding status. A broken red line surrounding an area indicates that nesting occurs irregularly within that range. This applies to opportunists, or nomadic nesters such as Cream-coloured Courser. Arrows indicate the direction of expanding colonisers such as Grey Francolin, Rose-ringed Parakeet and House Crow.

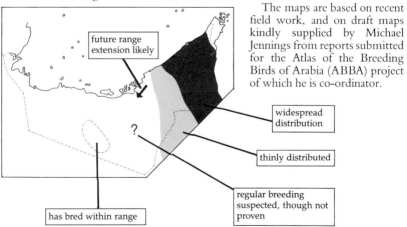

The maps are based on recent field work, and on draft maps kindly supplied by Michael Jennings from reports submitted for the Atlas of the Breeding Birds of Arabia (ABBA) project of which he is co-ordinator.

future range extension likely

widespread distribution

thinly distributed

regular breeding suspected, though not proven

has bred within range

Sequence and nomenclature

Generally the species' names and their sequence follow Voous (1977) in his *List of Recent Holarctic Bird Species* and Gallagher & Woodcock (1980). Some rearrangements have been made to suit the page layouts. Vernacular names represent current usage in Arabia with the exception of Yellow-legged and Armenian Gulls, which I have separated in the light of recent observations made around the Arabian Peninsula by Dr. W.R.P. Bourne. It is hoped this split may stimulate further interest and discussion on Arabian seabird distribution.

Migration Timings

The knowledge of a species' seasonal movements is essential before planning any field trip. It is also important to know what species you are likely to find, particularly if you are looking for something special. Most migrants have regular passage periods, varying with each country and region they pass through. They also have regular routes and resting places. Species that occur regularly in spring are not always present in such numbers in autumn, and this is true with many chats, warblers and shrikes. Conversely wader passage is very large and noticeable in autumn, but hardly reported in spring. The timings charts, which are based on actual records going back many years, reflect this.

Although the UAE is a relatively small country there is a significant difference between migration periods in the north and south, and particularly in movement over the Gulf islands within UAE territory. Indication of peak passage timings are based mostly on studies made in the Northern Emirates (particularly Dubai), while all known records are taken into account to spread the timings where necessary. A disproportionate number of rarities have been reported from Das and Dalma islands, and from Asab and Bu Hasa. Many late and early migrants also occur in these remote locations, which seem to attract these disorientated migrants. Unfortunately many areas are of restricted access to the general public.

Three shaded tones have been used in the timings charts to indicate relative frequency, and arrows and question marks have been inserted to indicate potential occurrence. Months are divided approximately into 10 day segments.

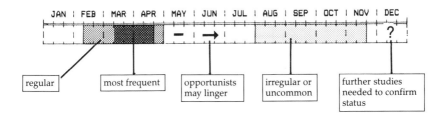

Status

The status of individual species is shown in code after the text of each. Where a species has more than one status, the sequence signifies order of importance. Upper case means it is usually common. (This does not apply for escapes and vagrants).

cb – casual breeder
mb – migrant breeder
pm – passage migrant
rb – resident breeder
sv – summer visitor (non-breeding)
wv – winter visitor

V – vagrant
E – escaped or recently introduced
? or ( ) – species requires further study to substantiate status

Glossary of local names used in the book

Barasti – palm fronds
Falaj – irrigation canal
Ghaf – thorn tree *Prosopis cineraria*
Jebel – hill/mountain
Khaleej – (the) Gulf
Khor – creek
Sabkha – saltflats
Wadi – (usually dry) river bed

Exotic introductions

S everal introduced species occur in the Emirates, many thriving in the rapidly expanding urban habitats around the Gulf coastal cities. In several countries 'exotic' introductions have practically taken over, pushing out endemic and other sensitive bird populations and this could happen too in the UAE.

Though still localised, the most commonly introduced species are Common Mynah, Rose-ringed Parakeet and Red-vented Bulbul. All are found around the urban coastal areas, particularly in Abu Dhabi and Dubai, with smaller numbers in Sharjah, Ras al Khaimah and Fujeirah.

There are few reliable reports which go back more than 40 years, and it is difficult to discover the origins of some sedentary species, particularly those of Indian or African origin. Rose-ringed Parakeet has become an agricultural pest in many places. Common Mynah is highly gregarious and flocks of up to 1,000 birds have occurred at favoured roosts in Dubai and Abu Dhabi. Bank Mynah also seems to be thriving, though in much smaller numbers, while there appear to be occasional eruptions of other mynahs, including Jungle, Crested and Pied Mynah all of which are likely to find suitable nesting habitat.

Red-vented and White-cheeked Bulbuls favour urban areas and often interbreed, producing confusing hybrids. Numbers of bulbuls do not seem to be increasing, or yet causing obvious problems. Partridges are popular introductions, and the most common is Grey Francolin. They are particularly widespread in the Northern Emirates, and have colonised most scrubby areas around large gardens and cultivations. Large numbers of Black Francolin, Chukar and other foreign game birds are being released in the spreading man-made woodland of Abu Dhabi's Western Region.

Finches and weavers are the next most common group. Some weavers have formed sedentary colonies, but mostly they turn up in early summer, their expatriate owners releasing them before departing on leave. Of finches, Indian Silverbill and other munias are generally the most common, and many are found feeding together, often with the remains of coloured dye still visible on their plumage.

A selected list of escapes is given on page 171 and many are covered in detail in the species text.

Acknowledgements

This book could not have been produced without the help and encouragement I received from a great number of people. I am especially grateful to Effie Warr for all the helpful advice willingly given over the 5 years I have spent researching the book. Her records, compiled from hundreds of correspondent's sightings have formed the basis for the main species text. Effie's co-operation also extended to checking the drafts and making many constructive suggestions which have contributed to the accuracy of the text.

Expert review of my drafts was given by a number of people, including advice on sections as follows: Dr. W.R.P. Bourne on seabirds and other pelagic species, John Uttley, Chris Thomas and Mick Green on shorebirds and Dr. Reza Khan on storks. I would particularly like to thank Michael Gallagher for his advice during the preparation of the breedings maps. These also include species distribution in adjacent areas inside Oman. His knowledge of the Gulf Region was also sought to check all UAE species' status, and review a number of old and unsubstantiated reports. Mike Jennings allowed me complete access to maps and other information in his possession. I am also grateful to Mike for his useful comments on my early map drafts. My thanks again to Effie Warr for also arranging access to the skin collection at the British Museum (Natural History) at Tring, and to Duncan Brooks for confirming the identification of several species, based on some very poor photographs.

I am grateful to Carolyn Lehmann for proof-reading final drafts, and Jenny Hollingworth who checked Emirates Natural History Group records, providing further evidence for the inclusion of a number of vagrants. Other people provided much useful information particularly Bish Brown, Adrian Chapman, Dave Robinson, Dave Suddaby and all birdwatching members of the Dubai Natural History Group and others who provided records. My appreciation and thanks go to all of them.

I would like to thank Bill Morton for his excellent line drawings throughout the species text, and Margaret Henderson for the superb cover illustrations and site views.

Without John Bannon this book could not have been published in its present form. His guidance in revising my early drafts and his patience in checking and rectifying text throughout the project has resulted in the production of one of Arabia's first birdwatching guides. In addition to his help in producing the book, John's friendship and good company on our field trips has made birding in the hot deserts and remote mountains of the Emirates quite memorable.

JANUARY – A lively lull

The Emirates have ample wetland sites, attracting large numbers of wintering wildfowl, waders and other waterbirds. Creeks, lagoons, reservoirs, sewage ponds and shorelines are teaming with all kinds of European and Asian migrants from August to April. Amongst the more common herons, ducks and shorebirds present, you are likely to find interesting visitors like **Black-necked Grebe**, **Spoonbill**, **Ferruginous Duck**, **Avocet** and **Pacific Golden Plover**. Less regular, and often hard to find, **Indian Pond Heron**, **Water Rail** and **Jack Snipe** occur in smaller numbers.

The mountains host a number of resident species unique to this habitat. On barren stony hillsides **Desert Partridge**, **Desert Lark**, **Pale Crag Martin**, **Hume's Wheatear** and **House Bunting** are likely to be found. **Scrub Warbler** is small and elusive, and occurs in ravines with minimal vegetation up to the highest peaks. **Yellow-vented Bulbul** and **Indian Silverbill** favour more fertile hillsides, plains and cultivations. Non-residents **Black Redstart**, **Red-tailed Wheatear** and **Desert Lesser Whitethroat** are common and widespread on tree-scattered hillsides and valleys. **Mourning Wheatear** and **Plain Leaf Warbler** can be elusive.

January sees a consolidation in seabird numbers. **Black-headed Gull** is abundant, and small numbers of **Great Black-headed Gull** can be found scavenging with them along shorelines. **Sandwich Tern** is common at this time.

Records indicate that around 160 species are regularly reported in January, a good challenge for a determined birder.

FEBRUARY – Preparations for departure

February sees a start of the return migration. Sensing the lengthening days, **Swallows** once again herald the start of spring. They are followed quickly by an influx of **Hoopoe** and **Yellow Wagtail**, and the first **Woodchat Shrike** is likely to occur by mid month.

Little Ringed Plover is an early northbound migrant, some remaining to nest. The pelagic **Red-necked Phalarope** occasionally occurs on inland pools, and some early **Garganey** pass through from mid month, the drake in immaculate breeding plumage.

February is also a busy month for the residents, some of which are already nesting. **Palm Dove**, **Indian Roller**, **Crested Lark**, **Great Grey Shrike** and **Brown-necked Raven** in inland areas, and **Rose-ringed Parakeet**, **Graceful Warbler** and **Common Mynah** in gardens and cultivations. These early nesters thus avoid the difficulties of raising young in the heat of the Gulf summer.

By the end of the month the numbers of winter visitors are augmented by new arrivals from the south. Some species such as **Skylark**, **Bluethroat**, **Black Redstart**, **Stonechat** and **Starling** decline in number as many start their northbound migration.

MARCH – Spring fever

By the end of March, winter is practically over. Bird migration goes into top gear and the evidence can be seen in all likely habitats throughout the Southern Gulf. Passage movement occurs east to west as well as south to north, and migrants arrive from the Indian sub-continent, Africa and southern Arabia.

Among these March migrants, many races of **Yellow Wagtails** arrive at damp habitats favoured also by **Red-throated Pipit** and **Water Pipit.** In gardens, parks and clearings **Pied Wheatear** is common, and **Redstart** appears from mid month, the eastern race (with white wing-patch) *samamisicus* arriving first. Numbers of **Isabelline Shrikes** increase, the males looking very elegant. **Woodchat Shrike** is present and there is passage of pale race **Great Grey Shrike** *L. e. pallidirostris*.

Numbers of warblers increase, with **Ménétries's Warbler**, **Lesser** and **Common Whitethroat** appearing in wooded areas amongst the abundant **Chiffchaff**. The end of the month sees a brief passage of **Semi-collared Flycatcher**.

Egg-laying reaches a peak for residents **Kentish Plover**, **Collared Dove, Palm Dove, Crested Lark** and **Graceful Warbler.** Male **Purple Sunbirds** now look magnificent in their glossy breeding plumage.

Most adult **Black-headed Gulls** depart, abundant and obtrusive in winter they leave behind a modest number of immature birds, which linger until summer.

Red-tailed Wheatear

Plain Leaf Warbler

Red-throated Pipit

Ménétries's Warbler

Semi-collared Flycatcher

APRIL – An exotic passage

Following the departure of most winter visitors, the number of species decreases but the actual number of birds reaches a peak as migrants pass through in continuous streams. It's a month for exotic sightings, with **European Bee-eater** and **Rock Thrush** making an early appearance, followed by **Nightjar**, **Blue-cheeked Bee-eater**, **European Roller** and **Golden Oriole**. Numbers of these species peak in late April and are regularly found in suburban parks, gardens and even on landscaped roundabouts.

Where there is sufficient damp cover, **Night,** **Squacco** and **Purple Heron** may halt on passage. **Spotted** and **Baillon's Crake** are regular visitors to ditches and overgrown marshes. **Little Bittern** is regular, often appearing to be nest prospecting, though breeding has not been recorded. **Garganey** is widespread, and a shy **Shelduck** or two are likely on lagoons and inland ponds.

Willow Warbler arrives to replace wintering **Chiffchaff**, the overlap causing some identification problems (the latter is generally more common). Skulking and difficult to observe, **Rufous Bush Chat** and **White-throated Robin** are likely to occur too at this time. By the end of the month **Red-backed** and **Lesser Grey Shrike** appear, adding to the list of shrikes which regularly occur.

One of the last and most common spring migrants to be found is **Spotted Flycatcher**, arriving at the end of April, its passage extending well into May.

MAY – The movement slows

Among the last migrants heading for the Asian mainland are **Turtle Dove** and **Hoopoe**. Some make the UAE their final destination, and as conditions become more favourable, breeding numbers increase annually.

Warblers are common in May, particularly **Marsh** and **Reed Warbler**, the former abundant some years. **Barred Warbler** can be expected early in the month in thicker, well-established woods.

Around cultivations and scrubby areas **Grey Francolin** raises its young from mid month, the tiny chicks often seen scurrying after their parents in the undergrowth.

Pallid Swifts are frantic at their nesting colonies, particularly Dubai Museum, where the hundreds of wheeling birds present a memorable sight at dusk.

There is more activity offshore. Many terns breed in the region and numbers increase at this time. They include **Swift**, **Lesser Crested**, **White-cheeked** and **Bridled Tern**. More common on creeks and mudflats, **Caspian** and **Saunders' Little Tern** are present too. Immature **Whiskered Terns** often visit inland lagoons and sewage plants in late spring and summer.

Of waders, **Sanderling** and **Common Sandpiper** depart, whilst breeding **Little Ringed Plover** and **Red-wattled Lapwing** are engaged in noisy territorial displays to protect their young.

JUNE – The end of the rush

The main passage is over, and it can be a time of sporadic sightings of stragglers.

Many birds in their first summer are not yet ready to breed and continue to wander or remain in their winter quarters. These include **Night Heron**, **Grey Heron**, **Purple Heron** and **Greater Flamingo**. A mixture of waders also choose to oversummer; **Lesser Sand Plover**, **Grey Plover**, **Little Stint**, **Bar-tailed Godwit**, **Redshank**, and **Turnstone** survive on the pickings of the Gulf's superheated mudflats, several thousand miles from their parents' Arctic breeding grounds.

Immature gulls and terns are likely at favoured inshore sites, **Slender-billed Gull** and **Sandwich** **Tern** being the most common.

Most good habitats will still provide some interesting sightings. In sandy scrub **Black-crowned Finch Lark**, **Bifasciated** and **Crested Lark**; in mountains, outcrops and escarpments **Pale Crag Martin**, **Hume's Wheatear** and **Brown-necked Raven**; in gardens and cultivations **Little Green Bee-eater**, **Indian Roller**, **Graceful Warbler** and **Purple Sunbird**; while in drier areas of scrub and acacia **Arabian Babbler** and **Great Grey Shrike** are widespread. Small numbers of **Olivaceous Warbler** breed locally.

Blue-cheeked Bee-eater

Rufous Bush Chat

White-throated Robin

Red-wattled Lapwing

Hoopoe

JULY – The first trickle of autumn passage

Breeding activity continues for several local species. **House Sparrow, Palm Dove, White-cheeked** and **Red-vented Bulbul, Graceful Warbler** and **Purple Sunbird** are still feeding young (some even nesting again), while juveniles and family parties of **Indian Roller, Great Grey Shrike** and **Crested Lark** are present everywhere.

Borders of shallow ponds and puddles host nesting opportunists **Little Ringed Plover**, often sharing a site with **Red-wattled Lapwing**, whose young may be just leaving the nest. Desert scrub is alive with the activities of **Black-crowned Finch Lark**, now forming small groups prior to dispersal (when flocks move to cultivations and more fertile open country).

Some of the first migrant land birds appear, **Swallows** leading the way in mid July. A larger migratory influx is evident on mudflats, marshes, creeks and other wet areas, which see the beginning of a shorebird invasion. After the end of the short Arctic summer, numbers of **Little Stint, Curlew Sandpiper, Bar-tailed Godwit** and **Curlew** arrive at coastal locations. At the end of the month, pools and pond margins welcome autumn's first **Common Sandpipers** often accompanied by less-common **Green** and **Wood Sandpipers**.

AUGUST – A taste of what's to come

This is the month when most birds probably start their migration, in some cases after their summer moult. The end of the month can be very promising as numbers build up, and the likelihood of sightings of tired and hungry migrants increases.

August is a good time for wader-watching and suitable sites can host over 20 species. The passage of **Curlew Sandpiper** is very evident, most refuelling before continuing on to African wintering grounds. Large flocks of **Lesser** and **Greater Sand Plover, Grey Plover** and **Redshank** may also be seen.

Terns are common; **Sandwich** and **Saunders' Little Tern** on sandbanks and creeks, **Swift, Lesser Crested** and **White-cheeked Terns** on sheltered shorelines and sea coasts. **Bridled Tern** is more difficult to find, but individuals often join in with the opportunist flocks when fishermen haul in their catches during a beach trawl.

Inland ponds and pools are good sites for **Garganey, Collared Pratincole, Little Ringed Plover, Ruff, Whimbrel, Turnstone** and **Red-necked Phalarope,** some halting only briefly on passage. **Squacco** and **Purple Heron** are likely to be found at pools and marshes, and **Grey Heron** are common at all suitable sites.

Parks, gardens and cultivations attract **European Roller, Hoopoe, Nightingale, Isabelline Wheatear, Clamorous Reed Warbler, Olivaceous Warbler** and **Golden Oriole. Blue-cheeked** and **European Bee-eater** are likely too, colourful bonuses to the month's list of exotics.

SEPTEMBER – The rush becomes a flood

A sudden peak is reached for variety and numbers of migrants. A good average for the month, recorded by an active birdwatcher might be 145 species – a respectable figure for such a desert region.

Large irrigated gardens and parks attract the greatest variety of birds, their abundant insect food supply suiting passerines and others too. Here you will find **Turtle Dove, European Roller, Tawny Pipit, Yellow Wagtail** (of many races), **Nightingale, Olivaceous Warbler, Common Whitethroat, Garden Warbler, Spotted Flycatcher, Isabelline Shrike, Rose-coloured Starling** and **Ortolan Bunting**. In the sky look for **European Bee-eater, Sand Martin** and **House Martin**.

Desert scrub too has its attractions for migrants such as **Short-toed Lark, Whinchat, Desert Wheatear** and **Blue Rock Thrush**.

Many herons, which are strongly migratory, occur. **Little Bittern, Night Heron** and **Little Egret** can be found at freshwater pools with overgrown borders, or even a wet wadi. Mudflats attract **Great White Egret** and **Spoonbill**. Small numbers of **Glossy Ibis** are likely too. The normally coastal **Little Green Heron** moves inland, some favouring pools and marshes. Numbers of **Garganey, Green** and **Wood Sandpiper** and **Turnstone** increase.

From the middle of the month most large grassy areas are a mass of such waders as **Ringed Plover, Kentish Plover, Pacific Golden Plover, Little Stint, Ruff, Snipe, Whimbrel, Curlew** and **Turnstone**. Rarer visitors have also been recorded, including **Caspian Plover** and **Dotterel**. Less scarce, but never common **White-tailed Plover** usually arrives at the end of the month.

Graceful Warbler

Short-toed Lark

Isabelline Shrike

Clamorous Reed Warbler

Tawny Pipit

OCTOBER – The seasonal transition

As autumn makes way for winter in the Gulf, the changes are slow. There are no obvious signs such as leaves turning brown, or a premature fall of snow heralding the start of winter. Many migrants now arriving in the Emirates are likely to overwinter, and many species are noted for the first time since their departure the previous March.

Of the larger birds the most important group are the ducks. Formerly quite scarce winter visitors to this arid region, several species now regularly occur from mid October, including **Wigeon**, **Teal** (the most numerous), **Mallard**, **Pintail** and **Shoveler**. They are found on creeks, inland ponds, sewage plants and even large swimming pools! Less regular are diving ducks **Pochard**, **Ferruginous** and **Tufted Duck**.

Wader movement is most significant at this time, notably the proportion of **Broad-billed Sandpipers** which arrive at favoured sites. Particularly Khor Dubai, where about 4000 were recorded in October 1986. This total forms a large proportion of the known Scandinavian population and yet very little is known about their wintering quarters, or migration routes.

A long distance traveller, **Pacific Golden Plover** arrives from north-eastern Siberia, to be found on damp meadows and some tidal mudflats. Many pipits and wagtails arrive in October, the commonest is **Tree Pipit** on passage, followed in late October by wintering **Red-throated Pipit** and **White Wagtail. Isabelline Shrike** is likely to be found in cultivations and parks, hunting from a shady perch.

NOVEMBER – Settling in

Many migrants arrive in November to overwinter in the Emirates, and of this month's more common winter visitors **Skylark**, **Water Pipit**, **Black Redstart**, **Stonechat**, **Song Thrush** and **Starling**, few will stay later than March.

At sheltered coastal sites, and at pools, ponds and flooded dumps **Black-necked Grebe**, **Great Cormorant**, **Coot** and **Kingfisher** can be found. And following the October invasion of **Lesser Black-backed** and **Yellow-legged Gulls**, now **Black-headed Gulls** join the scavengers on creeks and mudflats. In non-breeding plumage they are often confused with the ever-present **Slender-billed Gull**.

It can be an exciting month too, with several unusual species recorded in recent years. These include **Red-breasted Merganser**, **Great Knot**, **Rufous Turtle Dove**, **Richard's**, **Long-billed** and **Pechora Pipit**, **Hypocolius**, **Mourning Wheatear** and **Black-throated Thrush**. Many of these have been found away from the Gulf towns, in areas seldom visited and little studied by birdwatchers.

Of raptors, **Pallid Harrier**, **Long-legged Buzzard** and **Spotted Eagle** are likely to be found on passage, and local **Ospreys** are already nesting on some islands and rocky crags.

DECEMBER – A temperate time for watching

December is probably one of the most pleasant months to be out-of-doors enjoying the birdlife.

Palm Dove and **House Sparrow** are already active, and some even start to nest, although their main breeding season does not begin until March.

On tidal creeks and mudflats a number of species predominate. Most wader flocks are made up of **Ringed** and **Grey Plover**, **Little Stint**, **Dunlin**, **Bar-tailed Godwit**, **Curlew** and **Redshank**. Along the coasts **Sooty**, **Black-headed**, **Yellow-legged** and **Armenian Gull** are present, while flocks of **Sandwich Tern** hunt over the fish shoals.

On some islands **Socotra Cormorant** are in the middle of their nesting season, and vast flocks are often seen from the mainland.

Areas of scrub and semi-desert, with scattered *Acacia* and *Prosopis* trees, are favoured by wintering **Lesser Short-toed Lark**, **Desert Wheatear**, **Desert Warbler** and **Desert Lesser Whitethroat**. Look out too for residents **Hoopoe Lark**, **Crested Lark**, **Graceful Warbler** and **Great Grey Shrike**. More common in the northern and eastern Emirates **Grey Francolin**, **Chestnut-bellied Sandgrouse**, **Little Owl**, **Little Green Bee-eater**, **Indian Roller** and **Arabian Babbler** are likely to be found.

With such a variety of birds present, winter birdwatching in the UAE can be very rewarding.

Black Redstart

male **Desert Wheatear**

Red-breasted Flycatcher

Desert Warbler

Isabelline Wheatear

THE DESERT REGION

The arid desert areas of the Emirates are amongst the harshest in the world. In order to stay alive creatures must take advantage of every available resource. Air temperatures reach 120° F. on most summer days, so shade is a very important factor. Without it, warm blooded creatures like birds could not hope to regulate their body temperatures.

However, there is some respite available. The proximity of the coast to many parts of the region provides a welcome onshore breeze, and there is seldom a day without its coolness.

Some remote desert areas have a layer of fresh water only a short distance below the surface, creating oases of plant and animal life, even amongst the dunes of Liwa, on the very edge of the Empty Quarter.

Much of the inland areas consist of fine wind-blown sand of variable consistency. An extremely small annual rainfall allows only a sparse covering of scrub to grow, while indigenous ghaf *Prosopis cineraria* and acacia trees dot the landscape, providing just enough shade, shelter and nesting sites for a small number of very hardy and adaptable species.

Great Grey Shrike occurs everywhere here, wherever an isolated tree provides a vantage point and likely nest site. The same applies to **Brown-necked Raven**, a widespread desert resident and scavenger, which is quite at home even in the most remote areas. **Black-crowned Finch Lark** and **Hoopoe Lark** favour sandy desert areas and are often common away from habitation. In winter **Desert Warbler** is one of the few passerines to be found feeding amongst the dry scrub.

In the Northern Emirates isolated cultivations will support a number of other interesting species,

Scattered Ghaf trees in the desert, near Al Habab, Dubai

including **Little Green Bee-eater**, **Indian Roller**, **Crested Lark**, **Graceful Warbler**, **Arabian Babbler** and **Purple Sunbird**. **Collared** and **Palm Dove** occur almost everywhere, while **Grey Francolin**, **Rose-ringed Parakeet** and **White-cheeked Bulbul** have recently spread into some quite remote cultivations. **Turtle Dove** is a breeding summer visitor to these areas.

Indian Silverbills often travel in nomadic feeding parties throughout the region, favouring even the most isolated cultivations.

Passage migrants are likely to be found at these oases, and amongst those already reported are **Hoopoe**, **Tawny** and **Tree Pipit**, **Yellow Wagtail**, **Rufous Bush Chat**, **Redstart**, **Pied** and **Desert Wheatear**, **Rock Thrush**, **Marsh**, **Reed**, **Olivaceous**, **Ménétries's** and **Orphean Warbler**,

Spotted Flycatcher and several species of shrike. However, because of the very nature of an oasis, tired and hungry passage migrants can occur at any time, and surprises are regular.

COASTS AND MUDFLATS

The Arabian Gulf shoreline is low-lying and indented by many creeks and inlets. There are no rivers which reach the sea and therefore no true estuaries, but a number of shallow tidal lagoons with their associated mudflats create a habitat which is identical to the estuarine sites of north and west Europe.

The absence of human disturbance on these rich feeding grounds makes these mudflats of great value to migrant waders. Of all the creeks of the Southern Gulf, Khor Dubai is probably the richest, and the most important feeding and resting area for passage waders. Other khors include Dhayah and Al Jazeerah Khor (Ras al Khaimah), Khor al Beidah (Umm al Quwain), Ajman, Khor Khan (Sharjah) and the lagoons around Abu Dhabi, all playing a vital role in the survival of long-distance Arctic migrants.

On most tidal mudflats, flocks of **Lesser Sand Plover**, **Little Stint**, **Curlew Sandpiper**, **Bar-tailed Godwit** and **Curlew** are common in late summer. **Greater Sand Plover**, **Whimbrel** and **Terek Sandpiper** are localised, particularly favouring sites at Umm al Quwain and Ras al Khaimah. Large flocks of **Dunlin** are common September to November. **Broad-billed Sandpiper**, a relatively unknown bird from northern Scandinavian and Russian breeding grounds, has been recorded in large flocks on Khor Dubai in late autumn. **Kentish Plover** is resident along most sheltered coasts, augmented by a large wintering population from breeding grounds on the Asian landmass.

Apart from waders, this habitat suits **Greater Flamingo**, present for most of the year on many

Al Jazeerah Khor, Ras al Khaimah, viewed from the dunes

lagoons, though breeding has not been recorded in Arabia since early in the century. A very sensitive and wary bird, it could one day nest in Dubai, following the construction of a nesting island in the centre of the Khor.

The Eastern Lagoon in Abu Dhabi has also been declared a nature reserve, the mangroves providing nest sites for residents **Little Green Heron**, **Western Reef Heron** and **Clamorous Reed Warbler**.

Other herons are found at coastal mudflats, the most common of which is **Grey Heron**, widespread from August to May, while **Great White Egret** is usually present in smaller numbers. Other birds likely to be found include **Spoonbill** and **Avocet** while **Great Cormorant** is present on sandbars and exposed mudbanks from November

to March. Gulls and terns are constantly in view, the most regular gull migrants being **Lesser Black-backed** and **Yellow-legged,** until the arrival of large numbers of **Black-headed Gulls** in November and December. **Slender-billed Gull, Gull-billed, Caspian, Sandwich** and **White-cheeked Tern** are present inshore for most of the year. **Whiskered** and **White-winged Black Tern** favour some coastal mudlfats as well as their more traditional freshwater habitat of inland ponds and lakes.

Seawatching will log a number of pelagic species, including **Pomarine** and **Arctic Skua, Sooty Gull, Swift** and **Bridled Tern,** and if fortunate, **Red-billed Tropicbird.** Mass movements of **Socotra Cormorant** are often visible from the coast.

PARKS AND GARDENS

Those familiar with the Emirates will know of the government's strong commitment to creating lush landscapes out of barren desert. A dramatic increase in the planting of trees by the municipal authorities has encouraged an unprecedented increase in the number and variety of birds in recent years. Irrigation water, some of which is a product of recycled sewage effluent, is a major asset and very little is wasted.

These days fresh water is widely produced by desalination plants. At Jebel Ali the energy-efficient aluminium smelter provides water as a by-product of the cooling process, and most of Dubai's water supply is produced there. Whatever the source, the cost of water is probably a small price to pay for the creation of a sub- tropical landscape, with all its beauty and benefits.

The numbers of birds and the variety of species are directly proportional to the amount of water available. Sometimes it is not enough to have areas of man-made woodland or tree-lined avenues. A nearby pond or an area of flooded grassland would greatly increase the site's potential.

The Northern Emirates attracts a great number of species, a result of its location on the horn of Eastern Arabia and its relatively varied and fertile landscape. Within a 30 kilometre radius of the centre of Dubai, over 300 species are regularly drawn to the sprawl of parks and gardens reaching along the Gulf coast.

Saffa Park, Dubai, looking south towards irrigation lake in 1988

230 species have been recorded in just six years at Saffa Park, only 12 kilometres from the city centre. The Emirates golf club has also achieved the correct formula to attract passage migrants – a combination of varied vegetation, ponds, grassland and careful management. The huge plot is easily visible to tired and hungry birds on high-level passage.

In Abu Dhabi increasing areas of man-made parkland and semi-woodland, such as Bateen Wood, are becoming more and more attractive to passage migrants and resident species alike.

Private gardens however, are most important to local breeding species. Lacking picnickers, pesticides and people there is seldom disturbance in a sympathetically-managed garden. Birds are often protected and jealously guarded within the confines of a householder's domain. Breeding species such as **Palm Dove**, **Rose-ringed Parakeet**, **White-cheeked** and **Red-vented Bulbul**, **Graceful Warbler**, **Purple Sunbird** and **House Sparrow** thrive.

These garden and park habitats appear quite unnatural in this desert region, but without them many migrant species would have to fly on to other more hospitable areas, or suffer starvation. New species to the region are recorded annually, a trend which is likely to continue as long as present attitudes remain, and the blooming of the Emirates continues.

MOUNTAINS AND WADIS

The Hajar mountains to the east and north, with their remote and isolated peaks, pose a specific challenge to wildlife. The dry, scrub-scattered slopes may appear desolate, but are vital for the survival of some very specialised species. **Hume's Wheatear** is perfectly suited to these conditions, its black and white plumage serving as an ideal camouflage in the sharp contrasts of sun and shade produced by the crumbling rocky hillsides.

The surface temperatures in mid summer can be very high, bringing about huge stresses in the rocks as they expand and contract. In spring and autumn the day and night temperatures are most extreme,

and a large number of cracks and ledges are likely to form, providing shelter for **Little Owl**, **Desert Lark** and **Pale Crag Martin**. Large ledges can host **Lappet-faced Vulture**, **Long-legged Buzzard** and **Bonelli's Eagle**, all known to favour this habitat for nesting, though little is known of their movements and distribution. **Eagle Owl** is found on some outcrops and foothills.

Steep ravines, formed by infrequent but violent water torrents pouring off the steep impervious hillsides, allow small bushes and trees a foothold in the cracks. Here, amongst the sparse vegetation **Scrub Warbler** can be found, even on the highest

Near the head of Wadi Ham, Masafi

peaks. Migrant **Red-tailed Wheatear**, **Upcher's Warbler**, **Desert Lesser Whitethroat** and **Plain Leaf Warbler** also favour this habitat. **Arabian Babbler** is found on plains and wider valleys.

The commonest mountain species is **Desert Lark,** and **Sand Partridge** though common, is usually found only by chance. **House Bunting** occurs in small unobtrusive flocks outside the breeding season. Overhead soaring on the thermals you might be lucky enough to see an **Egyptian Vulture.** Somewhat smaller, **Kestrels** nest on some mountain crags and can be seen throughout the year.

Deep in the larger green wadis, the air is still and stifling, and the rich vegetation provides shade, where **Graceful Warbler** and **Purple Sunbird** feed. **Little Green Bee-eater** is likely to be found in most cultivations and fertile wadis. A common and vocal resident is **Yellow-vented Bulbul** *Pycnonotus xanthopygos*, flourishing amongst the date palms, lemon and pomegranate trees. **Indian Roller** is attracted to the stillness here, and its nasal call can often be heard.

ATLAS OF BREEDING BIRDS

R elatively little is known about many of the Emirates' 67 currently listed breeding species. Much fieldwork is needed to learn more about their distribution and nesting times. The breeding status of many UAE species has been accepted without even the discovery of a nest, so clearly there are gaps in knowledge. Large areas of land remain unsurveyed, where new species may be discovered, or an extension of range is evident. For example, over 15 species were adeed to the breeding list between 1980 and 1990.

Most residents nest from November to March, although opportunists continue nesting throughout the long hot summer, and may still be laying in September.

Oberservers who have breeding records should send them to:

Michael Jennings, Co-ordinator, Atlas of the Breeding Birds of Arabia,
1 Eastcourt, Burbage, Marlborough, Wiltshire SN8 3AG. United Kingdom.
Please refer to the Atlas squares as shown on the map below.

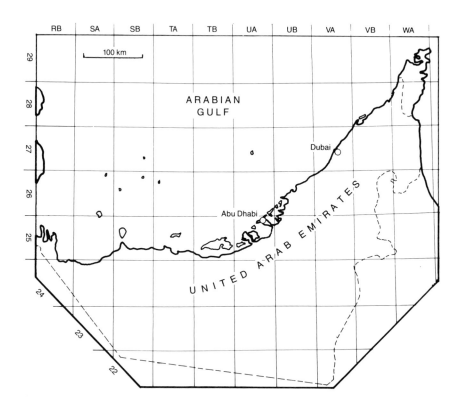

WHERE TO WATCH BIRDS IN THE EMIRATES

The Dubai area

The landscape is changing fast and good birding sites can develop with amazing speed in Dubai. There are some marvellous places to visit within only a short distance of the city centre.

Besides the major sites, many parks and gardens are planned for the 1990's, including a creekside park (between Maktoum Bridge and Garhoud Bridge) and a park at Hamriyah (on reclaimed land north of the old port).

The Jumeirah Beach Park was completed in 1989. It is situated 6 kilometres south of Dubai, and its small grassy open areas and clean beach attract waders, pipits and wagtails. The whole coastline here is a pleasant site for sea-watching early in the day.

The creek mouth, near the city centre is worth visiting in winter, when hundreds of seabirds scavenge around the fishing dhows, and along the harbour walls.

Rocky outcrops (qarns) about 60 km. along the road to Hatta, have resident colonies of **Desert Lark**, **Pale Crag Martin**, **Little Green Bee-eater** and **Eagle Owl**. The nearby desert is favoured by **Bifasciated** and **Black-crowned Finch Lark**. **Brown-necked Raven** is likely to be seen in the area.

The major sites in the Dubai area are as follows:

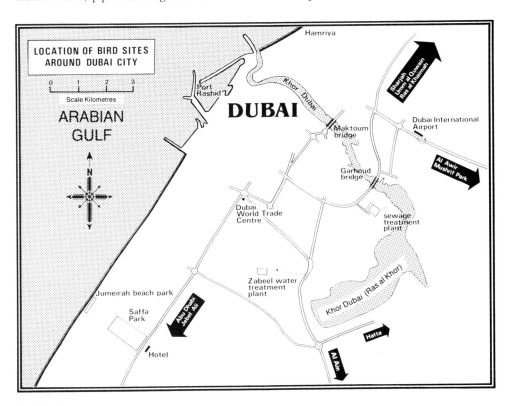

Saffa Park

Saffa Park was created in 1978 from a 70 hectare rectangular plot of barren salt flats and scrub, and over 230 species have been recorded there since its transformation. Its diverse and well-irrigated landscaping provides a truly mixed habitat which attracts tired and hungry migrants like a beacon. Nowhere else in the Emirates can any site claim such a selection, and on good days in spring and autumn over 45 species can be found in the park, in just one hour's birdwatching. In recent years, other large and often privately-owned gardens of this kind have tempted some birds away, but this site with its wonderful variety of species (particularly passerines) is still second to none.

Apart from the tree-lined avenues, and paths, the park is totally grassed with copses of casuarina and acacia over an expanse of open meadow. There are current plans to add more amenities and plant a further 4,000 trees which

28

Saffa Park

will undoubtedly attract a greater variety of warblers and other woodland-loving migrants. There are several interesting parts, one of the best being the original irrigation lake. Surrounded by trees and at times thickly overgrown, it shelters **Palm Dove, Rose-ringed Parakeet, Purple Sunbird** and **Common Mynah**, and during spring and autumn passage a good selection of warblers are likely to be found, including **Great Reed** and **Clamorous Reed Warbler** which often spend a week or more feeding in fallen trees at the water's edge. **Bluethroat** and **Nightingale** are regular visitors too. In winter **Black-necked Grebe, Coot** and a selection of ducks are present, including **Teal, Pintail, Pochard** and occasionally **Ferruginous Duck. Night Heron** often roost in the trees by day. **Common Sandpiper** is always present along the water line from August to May (one ringed individual has been recorded returning every year 1985-90) and in spring and autumn other attractions can include **Squacco** and **Purple Heron, Garganey, Spotted** and **Baillon's Crake, Green** and **Wood Sandpiper** and **Red-necked Phalarope.**

Another lively place is the south-west corner, behind the flying saucer-shaped pavillion. Here a cuttings dump provides food and cover for **Rufous Bush Chat, Black Redstart, Graceful Warbler, Ménétries's Warbler** and **Desert Lesser Whitethroat. Red-vented Bulbul** is resident, and **White-throated Robin** sometimes occurs on northbound passage from late March to April. **Rose-ringed Parakeet, Indian Roller** and **Common Mynah** often nest in damaged lamp-posts nearby.

The remainder of the park is also very rewarding. If the irrigation system leaks (particularly during autumn passage!), a mini-wetland is created, attracting **Collared Pratincole, Little Ringed Plover, White-tailed Plover, Common Snipe, Spotted Redshank, Marsh, Green** and **Wood Sandpiper** and at least four species of pipits, including **Red-throated** and **Water Pipit.**

The expansive meadows suit **Pacific Golden Plover,** which usually winters in small flocks. **Crested Lark** are common, and the open grassland is ideal for wintering **Skylark, Tawny Pipit** and **Isabelline Wheatear.** (These open areas may be lost after the proposed renovation, and many species may opt for the open fairways of the Emirates golf club).

The scattered trees abound with **Purple Sunbird,** and in season **Hoopoe** and **Tree Pipit** feed in the shade. **Isabelline Shrike** is a regular winter visitor, and **Great Grey Shrike** is common from August to January. Four other types of shrike have been recorded, mostly in spring, and **European Roller, Blue-cheeked Bee-eater, Golden Oriole** and **Semi-collared Flycatcher** rank amongst the park's colourful favourites. **Cuckoo, European Nightjar** and **Wryneck** are regular in spring and autumn.

Situated next to the Abu Dhabi road, 5 kilometres south of Dubai's Trade Centre roundabout, it is open from 6.30 a.m. to 9.30 p.m. every day, (but closed for the Holy month of Ramadan). Access is possible when other gates are closed, through the gardeners' entrance gate at the north-west corner. The best time to visit is Saturday to Thursday or early on Friday morning before the park becomes crowded. Good birdwatching months are August to early May.

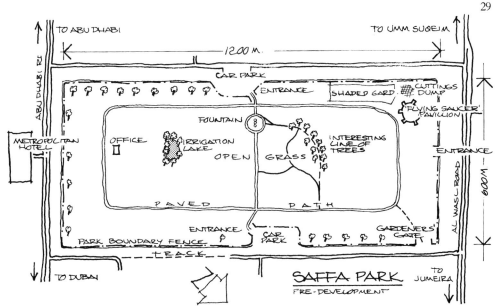

SAFFA PARK
PRE-DEVELOPMENT

The list of species recorded in the park since 1980 is impressive and also includes the following:

Little Grebe	Red-wattled Lapwing	Lesser Short-toed Lark	Orphean Warbler
Bittern	Sociable Plover	Sand Martin	Barred Warbler
Little Bittern	Lapwing	Swallow	Lesser Whitethroat
Cattle Egret	Sanderling	Red-rumped Swallow	Common Whitethroat
Western Reef Heron	Little Stint	House Martin	Garden Warbler
Little Egret	Temminck's Stint	Richard's Pipit	Blackcap
Grey Heron	Curlew Sandpiper	Meadow Pipit	Wood Warbler
White Stork	Dunlin	Yellow Wagtail	Chiffchaff
Glossy Ibis	Broad-billed Sandpiper	Citrine Wagtail	Willow Warbler
White-fronted Goose	Ruff	Grey Wagtail	Spotted Flycatcher
Greylag Goose	Jack Snipe	White Wagtail	Red-breasted Flycatcher
Shelduck	Woodcock	White-cheeked Bulbul	Isabelline Shrike
Cotton Teal	Black-tailed Godwit	Robin	Red-backed Shrike
Wigeon	Bar-tailed Godwit	Thrush Nightingale	Lesser Grey Shrike
Gadwall	Whimbrel	Redstart	Great Grey Shrike
Mallard	Curlew	Whinchat	Woodchat Shrike
Shoveler	Redshank	Stonechat	Masked Shrike
Brahminy Kite	Greenshank	Northern Wheatear	Indian House Crow
Marsh Harrier	Turnstone	Pied Wheatear	Starling
Pallid Harrier	Great Black-headed Gull	Black-eared Wheatear	Brahminy Mynah
Steppe Eagle	Black-headed Gull	Desert Wheatear	Rose-coloured Starling
Kestrel	Slender-billed Gull	Red-tailed Wheatear	Bank Mynah
Saker Falcon	Lesser Black-backed Gull	Rock Thrush	Spanish Sparrow
Peregrine Falcon	Yellow-legged Gull	Blue Rock Thrush	Tree Sparrow
Grey Francolin	Common Tern	Blackbird	Pale Rock Sparrow
Quail	Whiskered Tern	Black-throated Thrush	Yellow-throated Sparrow
Water Rail	White-winged Black Tern	Fieldfare	Rüppell's Weaver
Corncrake	Collared Dove	Song Thrush	Red Avadavat
Moorhen	Turtle Dove	Redwing	Indian Silverbill
Black-winged Stilt	Alexandrine Parakeet	Grasshopper Warbler	Siskin
Stone Curlew	Barn Owl	Savi's Warbler	Common Rosefinch
Cream-coloured Courser	Common Swift	Moustached Warbler	Ortolan Bunting
Ringed Plover	Pallid Swift	Sedge Warbler	Black-headed Bunting
Kentish Plover	Kingfisher	Marsh Warbler	Corn Bunting
Lesser Sand Plover	Little Green Bee-eater	Reed Warbler	Black Drongo
Greater Sand Plover	European Bee-eater	Olivaceous Warbler	Crested Mynah
Dotterel	Black-crowned Finch Lark	Booted Warbler	
Grey Plover	Short-toed Lark	Desert Warbler	

Khor Dubai (Ras al Khor)

Khor Dubai and Trade Centre

At the head of the tidal creek of Khor Dubai, 5 kilometres inland from the city of Dubai, a shallow lagoon provides the most important estuarine site in the region covering an area of about 300 hectares. At low tide the enriched mudflats provide ideal feeding conditions for thousands of migrant waders which are attracted to the site.

Khor Dubai has had a traumatic past, saved just in time from destruction by dredging in the late 1970's and subsequently proclaimed a wildlife sanctuary in 1985 following years of disturbance by hunters.

The Khor is well known for its flocks of **Greater Flamingo**, hundreds overwintering, and many remaining throughout the year, a result of the creek's plentiful supply of food and protection by a 24-hour police guard. A low sandy island has been built to encourage their nesting, following a 1985 study by the British Trust for Ornithology, who reported favourably on the creek's potential as a nest site. Hopefully a colony will form in the coming years.

Over 80 species have been recorded on the Khor. Flocks of **Ringed Plover, Lesser Sand Plover, Grey Plover, Little Stint, Dunlin, Bar-tailed Godwit, Curlew** and **Redshank** overwinter, and late summer brings large numbers of **Curlew Sandpiper**, with smaller flocks of **Greater Sand Plover, Whimbrel** and **Turnstone**. Other visiting waders include **Avocet, Black-tailed Godwit** and **Terek Sandpiper**. **Kentish Plover** is resident, and numbers greatly increase in winter when migrants arrive from more northerly breeding grounds.

Khor Dubai is a major site for observing **Broad-billed Sandpiper**. Previously over-looked in such numbers, 4,000 were discovered on passage in October 1986 when it was apparent that a significant proportion of the western Broad-billed population depended on Khor Dubai as a migratory refuelling stop. Some are also present in winter and spring.

Wintering ducks include **Wigeon, Teal, Mallard, Pintail** and **Shoveler**. **Shelduck** often turns up in mid-winter, though usually only in ones and twos. A good selection of herons too provide much interest, including the confusing white and grey morphs of **Western Reef Heron**, in its white-phase resembling **Little Egret** (which occurs more regularly at freshwater margins). **Grey Heron** is common, while **Great White Egret** are scattered around in smaller numbers at low tide. **Spoonbill** are usually found standing in tight groups, sleeping. **Osprey** is a regular visitor throughout the year, and in late autumn and winter **Marsh Harrier** hunts over the Khor.

Gulls and terns are abundant from September to April, and in the summer large numbers of non-breeding **Sandwich Terns** form roosts on the mud spits. **Great Black-headed Gull** is a frequent winter visitor from December, and **Slender-billed Gull** is present all year round. Other visiting terns include **Gull-billed, Caspian, Lesser Crested, White-cheeked, Whiskered** and **White-winged Black Tern**.

The light is ideal for observing in mid afternoon, when the sun is well placed, and there are a number of promontories from which closer views can be obtained. On one causeway there is a colony of **Mallard**, introduced in recent years and now resident at the duck-feeder on the west side.

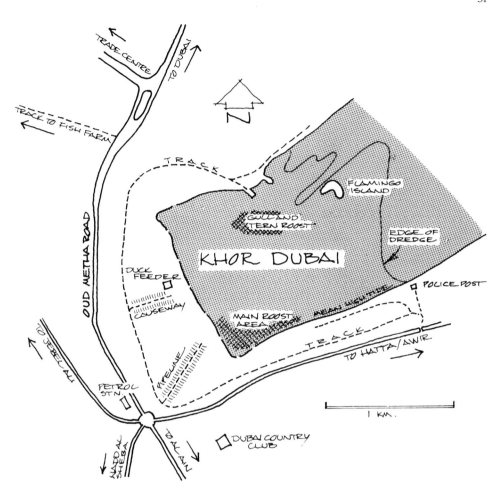

A number of other species have also occurred, including the following:

Little Grebe	Tufted Duck	Black-winged Pratincole	Greenshank
Red-necked Grebe	Spotted Eagle	Little Pratincole	Common Sandpiper
Black-necked Grebe	Steppe Eagle	Pacific Golden Plover	Red-necked Phalarope
Great Cormorant	Hobby	White-tailed Plover	Black-headed Gull
Little Green Heron	Saker Falcon	Sanderling	Lesser Black-backed Gull
White Stork	Peregrine Falcon	Temminck's Stint	Swift Tern
Glossy Ibis	Oystercatcher	Ruff	Common Tern
Greylag Goose	Black-winged Stilt	Spotted Redshank	Saunders' Little Tern
Garganey	Collared Pratincole	Marsh Sandpiper	

Mushrif National Park

Mushrif Park

This area of natural woodland has been designated a National Park by the Dubai Government. It is entirely fenced, with a single entrance gate open from 6.30 a.m. to 9.30 p.m. every day, (but is likely to be closed during some islamic holidays and the Holy Month of Ramadan). Situated 12 kilometres from Dubai International Airport on the road to Al Awir, the approach road is marked by a stone sign on the right-hand side.

This natural habitat is one of the Emirates' best examples of ghaf *Prosopis cineraria*, woodland, growing in a sheltered hollow over a series of ancient wells, surrounded by an impressive area of wind-blown sand dunes. An irrigation system has been installed and amenities include a swimming pool, theme areas and a restaurant, which are popular attractions, making the park rather crowded at weekends. There is a system of good roads throughout the park, including car

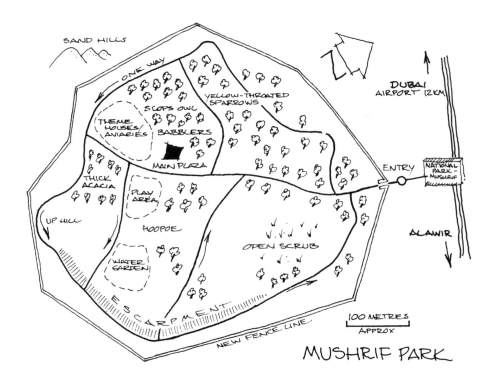

MUSHRIF PARK

parks and picnic sites, and concrete bollards prevent damage to the natural vegetation.

The car can be an ideal 'hide' for birdwatching. However, an occasional foray into the more isolated areas on foot can be most rewarding. There is grass around the amenity areas and plenty of low scrub and ground cover for residents **Graceful Warbler** and **Arabian Babbler**, and for winter visitors **Orphean Warbler** and **Desert Lesser Whitethroat**. The park is always alive with the calls of **Grey Francolin**, which breed here.

It is also a favourite site for **Little Green Bee-eater**, usually present in small flocks, and likely to be heard if not immediately seen. Good views of them can make a trip here most worthwhile. A small colony of **White-cheeked Bulbuls** are likely to be found around the central landscaped area.

In winter, eastern race (red-bellied) **Black Redstart**, **Song Thrush** and **Chiffchaff** are common throughout the thicker areas of vegetation. **Little Owl** breeds nearby and **Bruce's Scops Owl** can be found in autumn and early spring, usually by chance if disturbed from its roost.

The park attracts a variety of summer visitors, the most widespread being **Yellow-throated Sparrow**, a challenge to separate from **House Sparrow**, and usually located from mid April by its distinctive call. This ideal habitat attracts regular migrants **Hoopoe** and **Rufous Bush Chat**, and some remain to nest.

Other residents include **Collared Dove**, **Palm Dove**, **Indian Roller**, **Crested Lark**, **Purple Sunbird**, **Great Grey Shrike** and **Indian Silverbill**.

In addition the following species have occurred in and around the park in the last few years:

Sparrowhawk	Swallow	Pied Wheatear	Spotted Flycatcher
Kestrel	Tawny Pipit	Desert Wheatear	Golden Oriole
Turtle Dove	Tree Pipit	Rock Thrush	Isabelline Shrike
Rose-ringed Parakeet	Meadow Pipit	Blue Rock Thrush	Lesser Grey Shrike
Common Swift	Water Pipit	Marsh Warbler	Woodchat Shrike
Pallid Swift	Yellow Wagtail	Reed Warbler	Masked Shrike
Blue-cheeked Bee-eater	White Wagtail	Olivaceous Warbler	Brown-necked Raven
European Bee-eater	Redstart	Ménétries's Warbler	
European Roller	Stonechat	Common Whitethroat	
Black-crowned Finch Lark	Northern Wheatear	Willow Warbler	

Zabeel water treatment plant (fish farm)

Zabeel water treatment plant

The Zabeel water treatment plant is well placed, in an area of rolling scrub with scattered ghaf trees, only two kilometres from Khor Dubai. There are four large settlement ponds, also used for fish farming projects and the conditions could hardly be better. The total number of species recorded here so far is over 170, remarkable for so small a site.

The ponds are usually rich and healthy, attracting grebes, herons and wildfowl for most of the year. Twelve duck and ten heron species have been recorded here, including rarities eastern **Greylag Goose** and **Red-crested Pochard**.

Other species of interest recorded around the site include **Wryneck**, **Red-rumped Swallow**, **Citrine Wagtail**, **Black-eared Wheatear**, **Rock Thrush**, **Isabelline**, **Woodchat** and **Masked Shrike**. The area attracts raptors, and the list is impressive – **Osprey** is present for most of the year, and **Marsh Harrier** is common October to April. **Pallid Harrier**, **Sparrowhawk**, **Long-legged Buzzard**, **Spotted**, **Steppe**, **Imperial** and **Booted Eagle**, **Lesser Kestrel** and **Peregrine Falcon** have all halted their passage to prey on the rich food supply provided by the ponds.

There are smaller fish-rich ponds at a lower level, amongst the sand dunes, the result of drainage and restocking of the upper ponds. Reed beds thrive and there is plenty of cover for crakes and snipes. Hundreds of **Teal** and dozens of **Grey Heron** winter here. In addition **Black-winged Stilt**, **White-tailed Plover**, **Temminck's Stint**, **Black-tailed Godwit**, **Spotted Redshank** and **Marsh**, **Green** and **Wood Sandpipers** may stay for weeks on passage. **Little Ringed Plover** nests nearby.

This is a favoured site of **Collared Dove** which is abundant in the immediate area. The surrounding trees also make ideal nest sites for **Palm Dove** (and occasionally **Turtle Dove**), **Indian Roller**, **Graceful Warbler**, **Purple Sunbird** and **Great Grey Shrike**.

A small population of feral **Mallard**, and other 'farmyard' birds are fed from dispensers positioned near the upper ponds providing enough to eat for many of the visitors too.

The ponds provide a good roost and bathing place for large numbers of **Black-headed Gulls** from November to March in addition to common **Lesser Black-backed** and **Yellow-legged Gulls**. **Slender-billed Gull** is seasonal and **Great Black-headed Gull** usually visits in winter. Regular visiting terns include **Gull-billed**, **Caspian**, **White-cheeked**, **Saunders'**, **Little**, **Whiskered** and **White-winged Black Tern**. Immature **Sandwich Terns** roost in variable numbers over the summer months.

The site is situated close to one of the royal palaces, and a number of unusual, mostly escaped species, including **Saker** and **Peregrine Falcon**, **Chukar** and **Brahminy Mynah** are regularly seen.

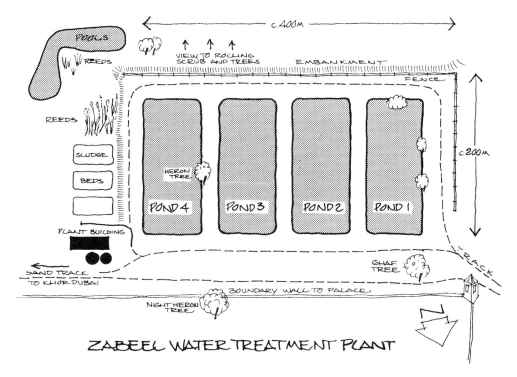

ZABEEL WATER TREATMENT PLANT

A number of other interesting species have been recorded at the site, including:

Little Grebe
Black-necked Grebe
Little Bittern
Night Heron
Little Green Heron
Squacco Heron
Cattle Egret
Little Egret
Great White Egret
Purple Heron
Glossy Ibis
White-fronted Goose
Shelduck
Wigeon
Gadwall
Garganey
Shoveler

Pochard
Ferruginous Duck
Tufted Duck
Brahminy Kite
Bonelli's Eagle
Hobby
Spotted Crake
Avocet
Stone Curlew
Collared Pratincole
Little Pratincole
Lesser Sand Plover
Greater Sand Plover
Pacific Golden Plover
Red-wattled Lapwing
Broad-billed Sandpiper
Jack Snipe

Whimbrel
Red-necked Phalarope
Sooty (Hemprich's) Gull
Short-eared Owl
Kingfisher
Little Green Bee-eater
Blue-cheeked Bee-eater
European Bee-eater
European Roller
Short-toed Lark
Red-throated Pipit
Water Pipit
Grey Wagtail
Rufous Bush Chat
Nightingale
Bluethroat
Redstart

Stonechat
Isabelline Wheatear
Pied Wheatear
Desert Wheatear
Rock Thrush
Sedge Warbler
Marsh Warbler
Clamorous Reed Warbler
Olivaceous Warbler
Ménétries's Warbler
Desert Warbler
Desert Lesser Whitethroat
Isabelline Shrike
Bank Mynah
Pale Rock Sparrow
Red Avadavat

Dubai (old) sewage treatment plant

Old sewage works, Dubai ~outflow

The old sewage works is located near the south-east bank of Dubai creek, just 'up-stream' from the Garhoud road bridge. Its future is uncertain following completion of a new sewage works on the Awir road. However, the old sewage works site is well-established and has a number of advantages. Its position as a catchment site for migrant waders is ideal. The vast mudflats of Khor Dubai are only 2 kilometres away and the sewage works lies between them and the sea.

From July to October, the settlement beds team with large numbers of palaearctic waders. They include **Little Ringed Plover, Kentish Plover, Little Stint, Curlew Sandpiper, Redshank** and **Turnstone**. Smaller numbers of **Black-winged Stilt, White-tailed Plover, Temminck's Stint, Broad-billed Sandpiper, Ruff, Spotted Redshank, Marsh, Green** and **Wood Sandpiper** also occur in the vicinity of the drying beds.

The ubiquitous flies attract a number of passerines too. **White Wagtail** is common from November to March, and **Citrine Wagtail** in its rather dull winter plumage is a regular winter visitor, often feeding alone near the damper areas. **Tawny, Tree, Red-throated** and **Water Pipit** are also likely to occur.

Elsewhere in the works gulls and terns can be seen in good numbers. Large flocks of wintering **Black-headed** and **Yellow-legged Gulls** are supplemented by **Great Black-headed Gull** in December. **Whiskered** and **White-winged Black Terns** hawk insects around the aereation tanks in spring and autumn. **Pallid Swifts** breed in some of the plant buildings.

The well-established trees provide shelter and nest sites for **Collared** and **Palm Dove, Graceful Warbler, Purple Sunbird, Great Grey Strike** and **Common Mynah.**

Outflow from the sewage process runs in a straight 400 metres long ditch into Dubai creek. The rich nutrient-filled water has created thick border vegetation, and a temporary home for numbers of migrants. Here, in season, are **Skylark, Meadow Pipit, Bluethroat, Stonechat, Ortolan Bunting** and a variety of warblers, as well as **Grey** and **Purple Heron, Teal, Spotted** and **Baillon's Crake. Little Ringed Plover** breed on the adjacent banks and **Little Green Bee-eater** are resident. Overhead **Sand Martin, Swallow, Common** and **Pallid Swift** are often present.

An opportunist colony of **Bank Mynahs** formed in spring 1988, making long nest holes in the outflow's sand banks. This was the first local breeding record of this species in many years.

Note: The future of this old sewage works is unknown. Since the opening of the new works the overflow ditch is often dry due to the reduced load. A bonus however is that the nearby Municipality nursery has been extended over some of the old settlement beds, and the whole site is still a great attraction, particularly to migrant passerines.

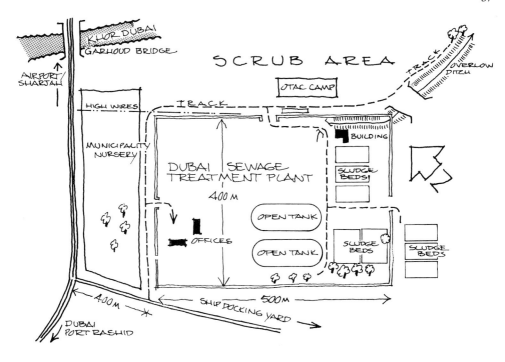

Other interesting species which have been recorded in and around the sewage works are as follows:-

Night Heron
Little Green Heron
Cattle Egret
Western Reef Heron
Little Egret
Great White Egret
Glossy Ibis
Spoonbill
Garganey
Marsh Harrier
Pallid Harrier
Long-legged Buzzard

Spotted Eagle
Osprey
Quail
Lesser Sand Plover
Greater Sand Plover
Pacific Golden Plover
Temminck's Stint
Jack Snipe
Black-tailed Godwit
Whimbrel
Gull-billed Tern
Caspian Tern

Lesser Crested Tern
Saunders' Little Tern
European Bee-eater
European Roller
Hoopoe
Short-toed Lark
Yellow Wagtail
Grey Wagtail
Isabelline Wheatear
Northern Wheatear
Pied Wheatear
Black-eared Wheatear

Marsh Warbler
Olivaceous Warbler
Ménétries's Warbler
Common Whitethroat
Spotted Flycatcher
Isabelline Shrike
Woodchat Shrike
Brambling
Black-headed Bunting

Emirates golf course

Bordered by 2,000 casuarina trees the Emirates golf club is one of the lushest 80 hectare plots of land in the Northern Emirates. Situated 25 kilometres from the centre of Dubai on the Abu Dhabi road, it is the latest contribution to the region's growing leisure facilities, and another course is planned.

It is also proving to be of great importance as a migratory refuelling stop, the green expanse of fairways attracting hundreds of palaearctic waders in autumn. Before the course opened to golfers in March 1988, 100 species were recorded in just four months. Of the four lakes, two are freshwater and stocked with carp, the other two are very saline, but all attracting a fair share of waders including **Lesser** and **Greater Sand Plover**, **Little** and **Temminck's Stint**, **Common Sandpiper** and **Red-necked Phalarope**. The ponds might attract many more species, but for the proximity of the busy tees and greens!

Little Green Heron, **Western Reef Heron** and **Grey Heron** are the most likely herons to be found, although the full list recorded is remarkable, including even **Little Bittern**, **Night Heron**, **Little Egret** and **Purple Heron**. From late July to October the fairways abound with **Kentish Plover**, **Ruff** and **Whimbrel** and the site attracted two **Dotterel** in October 1987 and 1988. One **Caspian Plover** visited in September 1988. In late summer hundreds of **Black-crowned Finch Lark** converge on the fairways, apparently to moult

and feed after the breeding season. By the end of September very few remain, only adding more mystery to this species' movements. **Hoopoe Lark** is regularly seen throughout the year, joined by a number of other migrants in late autumn. **Tawny Pipit**, **Isabelline** and **Northern Wheatear** are common and **Short-toed Lark** often makes an appearance in September, while **Skylark** overwinter from November to February. **Cream-coloured Courser** is likely in August and September.

The open fairways and scattered trees are attractive to shrikes too, with **Isabelline**, **Great Grey** and **Woodchat Shrike** already recorded, while of warblers, **Clamorous Reed**, **Olivaceous**, **Booted** and **Desert Warbler** may visit on passage.

The site also attracts raptors, the most regular being **Kestrel** and **Marsh Harrier**, while **Pallid Harrier** might occur in autumn. **Hobby** has been recorded in October.

Tree Pipit and **Yellow Wagtail** (of many races), are found in spring and autumn, and **White Wagtail** is very common in winter. **Richard's Pipit**, **Red-throated** and **Water Pipit** are likely to make appearances in autumn and early winter.

Other interesting visitors include eastern **Greylag Goose**, **Bimaculated Lark**, **Lesser Short-toed Lark**, **Semi-collared Flycatcher**, **Common Rosefinch** and **Black-headed Bunting**.

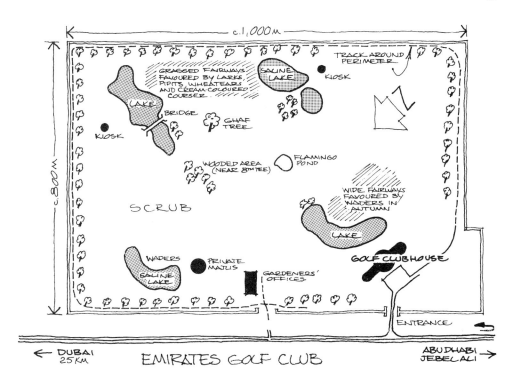

Other species recorded there are as follows:-

Black-necked Grebe	Broad-billed Sandpiper	Palm Dove	Marsh Warbler
Glossy Ibis	Common Snipe	Common Swift	Reed Warbler
Wigeon	Black-tailed Godwit	Kingfisher	Great Reed Warbler
Teal	Curlew	White throated Bee-eater	Ménétries's Warbler
Mallard	Spotted Redshank	Little Green Bee-eater	Desert Lesser Whitethroat
Garganey	Redshank	European Roller	Common Whitethroat
Shoveler	Marsh Sandpiper	Hoopoe	Willow Warbler
Osprey	Greenshank	Crested Lark	Chiffchaff
Spotted Crake	Green Sandpiper	Sand Martin	Spotted Flycatcher
Moorhen	Wood Sandpiper	Swallow	Purple Sunbird
Coot	Terek Sandpiper	Meadow Pipit	Golden Oriole
Black-winged Stilt	Turnstone	Citrine Wagtail	Brown-necked Raven
Collared Pratincole	Great Black-headed Gull	Bluethroat	Rose-coloured Starling
Little Ringed Plover	Black-headed Gull	Redstart	Common Mynah
Ringed Plover	Slender-billed Gull	Whinchat	House Sparrow
Pacific Golden Plover	Lesser Black-backed Gull	Stonechat	Indian Silverbill
Grey Plover	Yellow-legged Gull	Pied Wheatear	Ortolan Bunting
White-tailed Plover	Whiskered Tern	Desert Wheatear	Chestnut Munia
Lapwing	White-winged Black Tern	Ring Ouzel	
Curlew Sandpiper	Chestnut-bellied Sandgrouse	Song Thrush	
Dunlin	Collared Dove	Graceful Warbler	

Hotel Grounds, Jebel Ali

Hotel Grounds, Jebel Ali

A mongst the region's prime sites, the rich and varied habitat of the Jebel Ali hotel grounds has attracted over 120 species since records began in 1981. They are well-managed, and consist of an extraordinary variety of habitat, from woodland to coastal breakwater, thus providing for a wide selection of species.

The expanse of mixed woodland is the most interesting, a habitat rarely found in the region, sheltering a number of species not found regularly elsewhere. **Red-breasted Flycatcher** is often present in late autumn, occasionally wintering, while spring woodland visitors include the elusive **White-throated Robin** and **Semi-collared Flycatcher**. **Black Redstart**, **Song Thrush** and **Chiffchaff** are common in winter.

A variety of warblers occur on passage, including **Marsh Reed**, **Clamorous Reed**, **Olivaceous** and **Barred Warbler**. The most unusual visitors have been a **Purple Gallinule** in October 1984, **Siskin** in December 1985 and a **Black-throated Thrush** in April 1988. **Robin** has overwintered. Noisy and abundant, **Grey Francolin** are resident along with **Graceful Warbler** and **Purple Sunbird**. A small colony of **White-cheeked Bulbul** thrive here too.

The open clearings of irrigated grassland attract four species of lark, five of pipit, three kinds of wagtail and four of wheatear, in addition to numbers of waders in early autumn. The surrounding trees and shrubs provide hunting perches for **European Roller**, **Stonechat**, **Rock Thrush** and five species of shrike. **Hoopoes** feed in the shade, and **Bluethroat** favours the damp hedges.

Little Green Heron is resident, often hunting from the sheltered side of the marina breakwater. In autumn small numbers of waders feed on the quieter beaches. In the sheltered harbour **Coot** and duck may pause on passage, while **Socotra Cormorant** are present on the harbour wall from late autumn to spring, or in flocks of several thousand flying in lines offshore. A telescope is essential equipment for seawatching; a likely list would include **Gull-billed**, **Lesser Crested**, **Saunders' Little** and **White-cheeked Tern** in late summer and autumn, and **Slender-billed**, **Sooty** and **Great Black-headed Gull** in winter. Migrant **Arctic** and **Pomarine Skua** also occur on passage with the tern flocks.

Black-crowned Finch Lark and **Hoopoe Lark** nest on the scrub-covered dunes outside the hotel grounds.

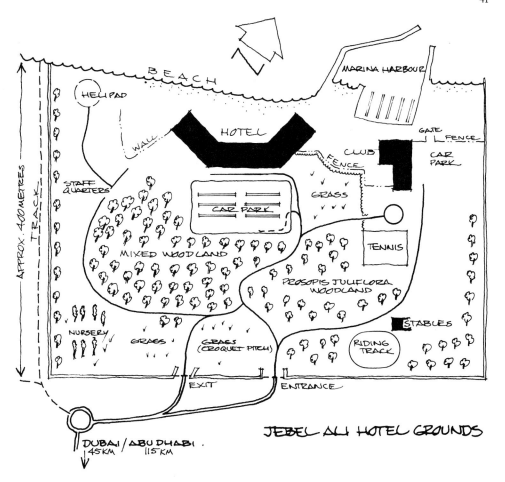

JEBEL ALI HOTEL GROUNDS

Other species recorded in the grounds include:-

Short-toed Eagle	Scops Owl	Redstart	Spotted Flycatcher
Marsh Harrier	European Nightjar	Whinchat	Golden Oriole
Osprey	Kingfisher	Isabelline Wheatear	Isabelline Shrike
Sanderling	Blue-cheeked Bee-eater	Northern Wheatear	Red-backed Shrike
Ruff	European Bee-eater	Pied Wheatear	Great Grey Shrike
Black-tailed Godwit	Wryneck	Desert Wheatear	Woodchat Shrike
Whimbrel	Short-toed Lark	Blue Rock Thrush	Masked Shrike
Green Sandpiper	Red-throated Pipit	Great Reed Warbler	Rose-coloured Starling
Caspian Tern	Water Pipit	Booted Warbler	Yellow-throated Sparrow
Bridled Tern	Yellow Wagtail	Ménétries's Warbler	Common Rosefinch
Whiskered Tern	Citrine Wagtail	Desert Lesser Whitethroat	Ortolan Bunting
Turtle Dove	Rufous Bush Chat	Common Whitethroat	Corn Bunting
Cuckoo	Nightingale	Garden Warbler	

Hatta

Hatta

120 kilometres south-east of Dubai, in the heart of the mountains, lies the enclave of Hatta. The area borders on the Sultanate of Oman, and easy access is available to some of the most interesting and beautiful mountain scenery in the region. This habitat is favoured by most of the local mountain species, and a lot more besides. Common residents include **Little Green Bee-eater**, **Desert Lark**, **Pale Crag Martin**, **Yellow-vented Bulbul** and **Hume's Wheatear**. Less common, and often on remote hillsides, a determined birdwatcher can find **Sand Partridge**, **Lichtenstein's Sandgrouse**, **Scrub Warbler** and **House Bunting**, all mountain residents.

The old town has a large area of date plantations, near the fort and adjacent to a series of springs which are tapped for irrigating the oasis. The mosque is here also and the spring is used as a washing place. **Indian Roller**, **Yellow-vented Bulbul**, **Graceful Warbler** and **Purple Sunbird** are resident, and migrants are regularly found.

The Hatta area receives more rain than the Arabian Gulf coast, and reservoirs usually form in Wadi Hatta, adjacent to the Oman-bound dual-carriageway. Small fish in the lakes attract herons, including **Western Reef** and **Grey Heron**, **Little** and **Great White Egret**. Wintering duck, **Black-necked Grebe** and **Coot** occur in the lower reservoir from November to March; **Little Grebe** are frequent visitors, and nesting has been reported. On the lake edges **Black-winged Stilt**, **White-tailed Plover**, **Temminck's Stint**, **Snipe**, **Greenshank** and other sandpipers can be found. **Kingfishers** are present in winter. Three **Cotton Teal** visited the reservoirs in February 1985.

Dam construction projects are changing the landscape and the habitat, and therefore the birdlife can be quite variable, often with pleasant surprises. Two opportunists, **Little Ringed Plover** and **Red-wattled Lapwing** have nested here, and are likely to occur following a good wet season.

The Hatta Fort Hotel is a complete landscaping contrast set amongst southerly facing foothills. Its superb gardens are a welcome sight to migrants. **Black Redstart**, **Red-tailed Wheatear** and **Blue Rock Thrush** are regular winter visitors, and **Indian Roller**, **Graceful Warbler** and **Purple Sunbird** are present throughout the year, the latter feeding amongst the profuse bougainvillaea. The gardens have had a strange effect on the shy **Hume's Wheatear** too, normally a bird of remote ravines and hillsides, it is regularly found perching on chalet roofs near the swimming pool!

Uncommon visitors to the grounds include **Indian Silverbill** and **House Bunting**. **Bonelli's Eagle** is occasionally seen soaring overhead.

In addition, a number of other species have been recorded in the area including:-

Great Cormorant	Marsh Sandpiper	Hoopoe	Desert Lesser Whitethroat
Wigeon	Green Sandpiper	Wryneck	Common Whitethroat
Garganey	Wood Sandpiper	House Martin	Garden Warbler
Shoveler	Common Sandpiper	Tawny Pipit	Plain Leaf Warbler
Ferruginous Duck	Greenshank	Water Pipit	Spotted Flycatcher
Tufted Duck	Common Tern	Yellow Wagtail	Isabelline Shrike
Egyptian Vulture	Saunders' Little Tern	Grey Wagtail	Great Grey Shrike
Marsh Harrier	Whiskered Tern	Redstart	Brown-necked Raven
Booted Eagle	Rock Dove	Stonechat	Pale Rock Sparrow
Grey Francolin	Pallid Swift	Marsh Warbler	Yellow-throated Sparrow
Spotted Redshank	Blue-cheeked Bee-eater	Olivaceous Warbler	

Sharjah

Birdwatching in the Sharjah area can be very rewarding. Apart from Khor Khan with its rich mudflats and itinerant waders and other waterbirds, the most worthwhile sites are all of Man's own unintentional creation.

Ramtha waste disposal site, 5 km. inland and near the Ajman border lies on the higher dunes at the head of a former high tide inlet which are now saturated salt flats. Enriched by thousands of gallons of sewage waste the resulting lakes provide an abundant supply of food for hundreds of birds. It is not surprising that **Little Grebe**, **Black-winged Stilt** and **Red-wattled Lapwing** have nested here, and the list of other recorded species is impressive. They include **Cattle Egret**, **Spoonbill**, eastern **Greylag Goose**, **Avocet**, **Collared Pratincole**, **White-tailed Plover** and **White-winged Black Tern**. The site also attracts quantities of wildfowl, herons, waders and gulls, while smaller land birds of all kinds are also common. The use of this site by the local authorities is likely to be temporary, and both birds and birdwatchers must take the opportunity while they can.

The water-table level in Sharjah is often high, and after rain many areas remain flooded for some time. The land around the cricket stadium is low-lying and ponds form, attracting grebes and ducks. **Moorhen** has bred in a flooded dump near the stadium.

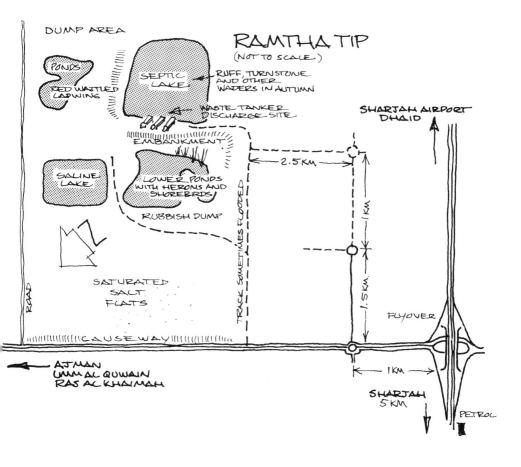

Khor al Beidah, Umm al Quwain

Khor al Beidah

The vast complex of lagoons and islands which comprise Khor al Beidah north-east of Umm al Quwain are the largest of their kind in the Northern Emirates. The birdlife here is spread over acres of shallow mudflats, mangrove swamp and scrub-covered dunes. It is varied and often abundant, best visited at high tide when many species form roosts closer to the shoreline. This is reached by following a choice of tracks over hard sabkha on the left side of the Ras al Khaimah road travelling north, shortly after passing the junction which leads to Umm al Quwain town.

A typical Gulf khor, there is a major influx of Arctic-breeding shorebirds from the end of July, when the mudflats attract flocks of **Kentish Plover**, **Lesser** and **Greater Sand Plover**, **Curlew Sandpiper**, **Bar-tailed Godwit** and **Redshank**. It is a favoured site of **Whimbrel** and **Terek Sandpiper**, both early migrants and likely to be found feeding near the shoreline for most of the year.

The lagoon is *the* site in the region for **Crab Plover**. A few are present all year, but they can number several hundred by mid winter. Often shy, they feed in loose flocks at the southern end of the khor, and may even nest nearby.

Western Reef Heron does breed amongst the mangroves on some of the islands, and a sizable colony of **Socotra Cormorant** nest nearby. Flocks of cormorants fly along the coast here in massive feeding sorties, and they are always present near the sheltered harbours of Umm al Quwain. Terns and gulls are common, including **Gull-billed**, **Swift**, **Lesser Crested**, **Sandwich**, **White-cheeked** and **Saunders' Little Tern**. **Slender-billed Gulls** often form large roosts on the mudflats.

Hoopoe Lark and **Crested Lark** nest on the dunes, and **Black-crowned Finch Lark** gather near the shoreline in late summer. Groups of **Short-toed Larks** sometimes winter on the saltmarsh scrub. **Little Green Bee-eater** breeds here too, in holes on the exposed faces of sand banks, and **Osprey** can be seen perched on a post or oil drum amongst the wader flocks just beyond the shoreline.

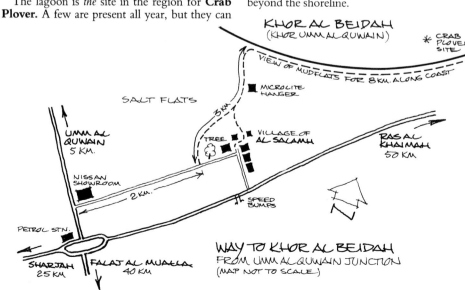

Other species recorded on the Khor and adjacent islands include the following:-

Black-necked Grebe	Marsh Harrier	Curlew	Kingfisher
Great Cormorant	Goshawk	Greenshank	Indian Roller
Little Green Heron	Spotted Eagle	Turnstone	Short-toed Lark
Little Egret	Coot	Great Black-headed Gull	Lesser Short-toed Lark
Great White Egret	Oystercatcher	Black-headed Gull	Sand Martin
Grey Heron	Ringed Plover	Lesser Black-backed Gull	Swallow
Spoonbill	Grey Plover	Yellow-legged Gull	Tawny Pipit
Greater Flamingo	Sanderling	Armenian Gull	White Wagtail
Greylag Goose	Little Stint	Caspian Tern	Isabelline Wheatear
Shelduck	Dunlin	Sandwich Tern	Pied Wheatear
Wigeon	Broad-billed Sandpiper	Barn Owl	Desert Wheatear
Mallard	Common Snipe	Common Swift	Graceful Warbler
Red-breasted Merganser	Black-tailed Godwit	Pallid Swift	Brown-necked Raven

Ras al Khaimah

There are a number of lagoons and tidal creeks north of Ras al Khaimah which have small populations of herons and waders. The mangrove-covered shoreline near Dhayah (opposite Rams) is very interesting. **Spotted Eagle** and numbers of **Marsh Harrier** often winter here, and **Lichtenstein's Sandgrouse** have been observed taking water at dusk. There is a small sandy creek at Ghalilah which usually attracts good numbers of waders and terns.

Southwards, on the way to Manama and Dhaid, extensive cultivations line the road after passing through Kharran, and between Digdaga and Khatt there are large open fields which support breeding **Red-wattled Lapwing**. Other species nesting in the area include **European Bee-eater, Hoopoe, Rufous Bush Chat** and **Yellow-throated Sparrow**. Residents **Little Green Bee-eater, Indian Roller, Yellow-vented Bulbul, Graceful Warbler, Arabian Babbler** and **Purple Sunbird** are common. Many more species are likely to occur from August to May and the area has great potential for vagrants and new breeding species.

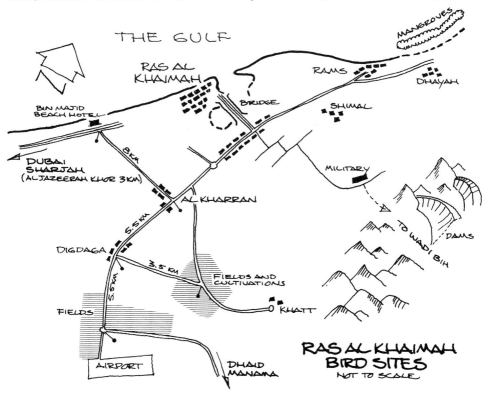

THE GULF

RAS AL KHAIMAH

RAMS

MANGROVES

DHAYAH

SHIMAL

BIN MAJID BEACH HOTEL

BRIDGE

MILITARY

DUBAI SHARJAH (AL JAZEERAH KHOR 3KM)

8KM

AL KHARRAN

5.5 KM

DIGDAGA

3.5 KM

TO WADI BIH

DAMS

FIELDS AND CULTIVATIONS

5.5 KM

FIELDS

KHATT

AIRPORT

DHAID MANAMA

RAS AL KHAIMAH BIRD SITES
NOT TO SCALE

Al Jazeerah Khor

Al Jazeerah Khor

The site is just south of Ras al Khaimah, adjacent to the old abandoned village of Jazeerah al Hamra, which sits on a promontory overlooking a system of mud islets and shallow creeks. There are a number of mudflats south of the village, and an expanse of shallow lagoons to the north, enclosed by a long mudbank just offshore. Al Jazeerah Khor (also known as Khor Qurm) is easily accessible from the main road, 3 kilometres north after the turn-off for Jazeerah al Hamra, and is recognised by a line of high sand dunes, which appear to guard the bay. The dunes rise to about 30 metres and provide an excellent vantage point for birdwatching.

The dunes are covered with scrub and acacia, a habitat well-suited to attract migrant passerines and favoured by an interesting selection of local residents. Truly an alternative source of interest if one tires of gazing at the selection of waders and seabirds on the creek below.

In autumn you are likely to find several hundred waders, including less common species **Greater Sand Plover**, **Whimbrel** and **Terek Sandpiper**. Small numbers of **Great White Egret**, **Spoonbill** and **Greater Flamingo** overwinter, and **Western Reef Heron** is present throughout the year. Massive feeding parties of **Socotra Cormorants** are a common sight here, flying in long V-shaped formations just offshore. **Marsh Harrier** and **Osprey** are regularly seen on the khor. On passage, **Spotted** and **Steppe Eagle** may be found soaring over the dunes. Resident on the dunes are **Grey Francolin**, **Little Green Bee-eater**, **Black-crowned Finch Lark**, **Hoopoe Lark**, **Crested Lark**, **Arabian Babbler**, **Purple Sunbird** and **Great Grey Shrike**. Other nesting species include **Hoopoe**, **Turtle Dove** and **Yellow-throated Sparrow**. **Indian Silverbill** and **Brown-necked Raven** often make an appearance.

Al Jazeerah is well situated to attract tired migrants, which are funneled along the coastal plain as the mountains approach the Gulf shoreline. Scarce migrants can, and do occur, often in good numbers. In spring, many warblers are present, feeding amongst the *prosopis* trees. The calls of **Marsh**, **Olivaceous** and **Orphean Warbler** are likely to be heard from February to May.

The site has great birdwatching potential and the species likely to be found may greatly exceed those so far recorded.

Other species recorded include the following:-

Great Crested Grebe	Sanderling	Gull-billed Tern	White Wagtail
Great Cormorant	Little Stint	Lesser Crested Tern	Black Redstart
Night Heron	Curlew Sandpiper	Sandwich Tern	Redstart
Little Green Heron	Dunlin	Roseate Tern	Pied Wheatear
Little Egret	Black-tailed Godwit	White-cheeked Tern	Graceful Warbler
Grey Heron	Bar-tailed Godwit	Saunders' Little Tern	Reed Warbler
Mallard	Curlew	Collared Dove	Ménétries's Warbler
Red-breasted Merganser	Redshank	Palm Dove	Desert Lesser Whitethroat
Short-toed Eagle	Greenshank	Common Swift	Common Whitethroat
Sparrowhawk	Turnstone	Pallid Swift	Chiffchaff
Oystercatcher	Great Black-headed Gull	Kingfisher	Spotted Flycatcher
Ringed Plover	Black-headed Gull	European Roller	Isabelline Shrike
Kentish Plover	Slender-billed Gull	Indian Roller	
Lesser Sand Plover	Lesser Black-backed Gull	Pale Crag Martin	
Grey Plover	Yellow-legged Gull	Swallow	

The Masafi area

Masafi

Masafi lies in a pass at about the 400 metre contour, in the centre of the Hajar mountain range which forms a barrier between the western facing desert plains of the Arabian Gulf and the eastern fertile coastal belt along the Gulf of Oman.

The Masafi area is predominantly mountain habitat, interspersed with cultivations and wadis. As such it is typical of the UAE mountains, favoured by a number of species which are rarely found elsewhere. Most of the surrounding mountains are dark and rugged igneous rock, with outcrops of pale cretaceous shale, the latter supporting the greater number of species. The vegetation is mostly goat-grazed acacia and scrub.

The calls of **Desert Lark** can be heard everywhere, even in the most remote areas, and small groups occur on the broken stony hillsides and adjacent gravel plains. **Yellow-vented Bulbul** and **Purple Sunbird** are common throughout. **Desert Partridge**, usually seen only when disturbed, favour the stony slopes. **House Bunting** breeds in the hills, and is likely to be found in small restless parties feeding with **Desert Lark** on hillsides or drinking in running streams, sometimes difficult to find. **Indian Silverbill** is also resident, though prone to wandering seasonally. **Hume's Wheatear** is widespread in the area, but strangely elusive in spring.

The pale cretaceous hills which stretch west of Masafi towards Dibba are generally of more interest to the naturalist than the surrounding dark peaks. Here, shrubs, acacia and grasses are more abundant. As a result, birdlife is more diversified and a number of migrants are likely to occur, including **Red-tailed Wheatear**, **Blue Rock Thrush**, **Desert Lesser Whitethroat** and **Plain Leaf Warbler**. **Yellow-throated Sparrow** breeds here and **Long-billed Pipit** is reported to nest high up on the rocky hillsides.

Resident in the bleaker areas are **Bonelli's Eagle**, **Lichtenstein's Sandgrouse**, **Eagle Owl** and **Little Owl**. **Brown-necked Raven** and **Pale Crag Martin** are resident too, joined on the crag by nesting **Pallid Swift** from early winter to spring.

In the cultivated lower valleys **Graceful Warblers** call, **Indian Rollers** occur around the palm groves and **Little Green Bee-eaters** hunt from prominent perches. About 8 kilometres north of Masafi on the way to Dibba, the road crosses Tayibah gravel plain, situated at the head of Wadis Uyaynah and Asimah. **Little Green Bee-eater**, **Arabian Babbler** and **Great Grey Shrike** are resident and numbers of wheatears, warblers and shrikes are likely to occur here on passage. Tayibah plain is a good site for raptors, and some smaller migrants choose the thorny savannah habitat in preference to the adjacent hillsides.

Other species recorded in this area include:-

Sparrowhawk	Scops Owl	Rufous Bush Chat	Booted Warbler
Kestrel	Common Swift	Black Redstart	Ménétries's Warbler
Peregrine Falcon	Hoopoe	Redstart	Desert Warbler
Grey Francolin	Wryneck	Whinchat	Orphean Warbler
Houbara Bustard	Lesser Short-toed Lark	Isabelline Wheatear	Chiffchaff
Rock Dove	Swallow	Northern Wheatear	Spotted Flycatcher
Collared Dove	Red-rumped Swallow	Pied Wheatear	Isabelline Shrike
Turtle Dove	House Martin	Desert Wheatear	Woodchat Shrike
Palm Dove	Tawny Pipit	Rock Thrush	Masked Shrike
Rose-ringed Parakeet	Grey Wagtail	Scrub Warbler	House Sparrow
Cuckoo	White Wagtail	Clamorous Reed Warbler	

The East Coast

Although Kalba is the most interesting area with the greatest variety of species, the coast road north to Dibba is a very attractive route with numbers of villages and cultivations worth exploring on the way. The road curves between the mountains and the sea north of Khor Fakkan and on the quieter beaches mixed roosts of terns can often be seen (six species are likely), and in late summer skuas and shearwaters are regular offshore.

The small town of Dibba lies on the border with Oman (as well as being tribally divided between Sharjah and Fujeirah). The fishing harbour usually attracts great avian activity, (not least of which are the indecent numbers of **House Crow**) and terns, gulls and some waders are common at most times of the year.

Over the unguarded border into Oman, the cultivations of Bayah are well-established and interesting. However the gravel plains further inland can provide some shyer species, including **Red-tailed Wheatear** in winter and **Eastern Pied Wheatear**, which has been recorded in autumn (and may occur too in winter). The area is still relatively unexplored and other uncommon species are likely to be found.

Khor Kalba and surrounding area

Khor Kalba

Khor Kalba is 12 kilometres south of Fujeirah, facing the Gulf of Oman. By far the most interesting site along this stretch of coastline, it is unique in many ways; not least of which is its area of extensive mangroves which thrive in the slack tidal flow on the upper reaches of the khor beyond the natural harbour.

This is the home of the **White-collared Kingfisher**, generally rare and localised in Arabia, and here belonging to a distinct sub-species found only in the Kalba mangroves. Best seen at low tide when it ventures on to the exposed mudflats of the inner lagoons, hunting from exposed perches on the southern side of the mangroves. No more than about twenty birds have ever been counted, so it is undoubtedly threatened, and measures must be taken soon to preserve its habitat.

Little Green Heron, **Clamorous Reed** and (probably) **Booted Warbler** breed in the mangroves too, their calls echoing amongst the thick vegetation, and competing with the screeches of the kingfishers.

The sheltered khor hosts a number of other interesting wintering species, including **Indian Pond Heron**, **Little Egret**, **Great White Egret**, **Greater Sand Plover**, **Whimbrel** and **Terek Sandpiper**. **European Kingfishers** are likely to be seen on low perches along the length of the khor, while **Osprey** and **Marsh Harrier** may hunt over the mangroves in search of food. Several species of tern including **White-cheeked**, **Lesser Crested** and **Swift Tern** are seen frequently around the breakwater at the harbour mouth. An **Indian Skimmer** occurred here in January 1988, a first record for the country.

Inland, at the edge of the gravel plains, are a series of pools. This is good habitat for **Temminck's Stint**, **Common Snipe**, **Redshank**, **Greenshank**, **Green**, **Wood** and **Common Sandpiper** from August to April, with a good mixture of additional passage waders in spring and autumn including **Collared Pratincole**, **Ruff** and **Spotted Redshank**. **Stone Curlew** is a regular autumn visitor. In addition **Citrine Wagtail**, **Water Pipit** and **Red-throated Pipit** are sometimes present at the pond edges, while **Long-billed Pipit** and **Desert Wheatear** have wintered amongst the adjacent scrub. **Red-wattled Lapwing** nests here from March to June and **Black-winged Stilt** raised young, recorded for the first time in 1988.

The savannah plains adjacent to the foothills often provide a whole batch of different species. **Little Green Bee-eater**, **Indian Roller**, **Pale Crag Martin**, **Yellow-vented Bulbul**, **Arabian Babbler**, **Purple Sunbird**, **Grey Grey Shrike** and **Indian Silverbil** are resident, while **Pallid Swift**, **Black-crowned Finch Lark** and **House Bunting** are present for most of the year. In spring **Pale Rock Sparrows** feed on the stony plain in small groups, and visiting **Yellow-throated Sparrows** nest in summer.

It is a good place to find **Blue-cheeked Bee-eaters** which are abundant in spring and autumn, some also breeding. Many head for the mangroves to roost at dusk.

Water-filled quarries and rubbish dumps on the plains behind the khor are also important sites where numbers of wildfowl and grebe overwinter. **Black-necked Grebe** is present some years November to March and **Little Grebe** may occur for most of the year, breeding when favoured conditions prevail. The biggest lake can be found amongst the trees on the inland side of the Oman-bound road.

Little detailed study has been done of the area, and much remains to be discovered about its abundant birdlife. **Great Knot** was first recorded here in autumn 1986, and other rare vagrants are likely to occur.

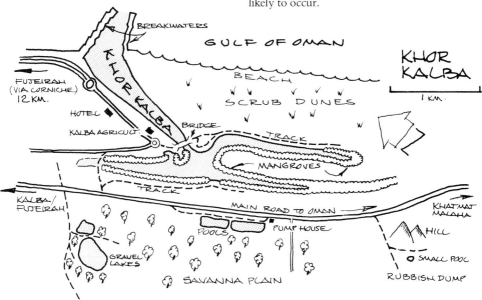

Recorded species are varied and interesting and in recent years include:-

Little Bittern	Coot	Bridled Tern	Black Redstart
Night Heron	Crab Plover	Saunders' Little Tern	Redstart
Squacco Heron	Little Ringed Plover	Whiskered Tern	Isabelline Wheatear
Cattle Egret	White-tailed Plover	White-winged Black Tern	Northern Wheatear
Purple Heron	Lapwing	Lichtenstein's Sandgrouse	Marsh Warbler
Glossy Ibis	Sanderling	Chestnut-bellied Sandgrouse	Reed Warbler
Shelduck	Curlew Sandpiper	Turtle Dove	Olivaceous Warbler
Wigeon	Broad-billed Sandpiper	European Bee-eater	Booted Warbler
Garganey	Black-tailed Godwit	Hoopoe	Ménétries's Warbler
Shoveler	Marsh Sandpiper	Hoopoe Lark	Spotted Flycatcher
Pochard	Red-necked Phalarope	Short-toed Lark	Isabelline Shrike
Pallid Harrier	Sooty (Hemprich's) Gull	Red-rumped Swallow	Brown-necked Raven
Sparrowhawk	Slender-billed Gull	House Martin	
Long-legged Buzzard	Gull-billed Tern	Yellow Wagtail	
Bonelli's Eagle	Caspian Tern	Bluethroat	

50

The Abu Dhabi area

There are a number of interesting places in the Abu Dhabi area which are certainly worth exploring. The protected reserve of the Eastern Lagoon is a prime site for herons, waders, gulls, terns and an occasional passing raptor. The mangroves provide shelter for nesting **Little Green Heron**, **Western Reef Heron** and **Clamorous Reed Warbler**.

Around the western tip of the island, including the Khalidiyah spit (with its ladies beach), the Royal yacht base and nearby hotel gardens you are likely to come across pipits, warblers, wheatears and shrikes. The shallow lagoons off this promontory and around Hodairiyat island are alive with waders and seabirds. **Osprey** and **White-cheeked Tern** nest here and sometimes **Crab Plover** can be seen around the quieter shorelines. Skuas are often reported offshore.

Grassy landscaped gardens near Buteen airbase attract waders, hirundines, pipits, wagtails and a selection of other migrants. The wide central reservations of Saeed bin Tahnoun Street are likely to favour similar fare, and **Cattle Egrets** sometimes overwinter in the area.

Al Wathba camel race track, on the 'truck road' to Al Ain, is the nearest interesting mainland site (about 40 km. from Abu Dhabi). There are extensive tree plantations on the approach road and on the southern slopes behind the grandstand. Grass fodder fields occupy much of the area inside the race track boundary. A selection of resident larks and other breeding species can be found here, including **Rufous Bush Chat**, which probably nests in the woods. **Egyptian Nightjar** was recorded here in August 1989.

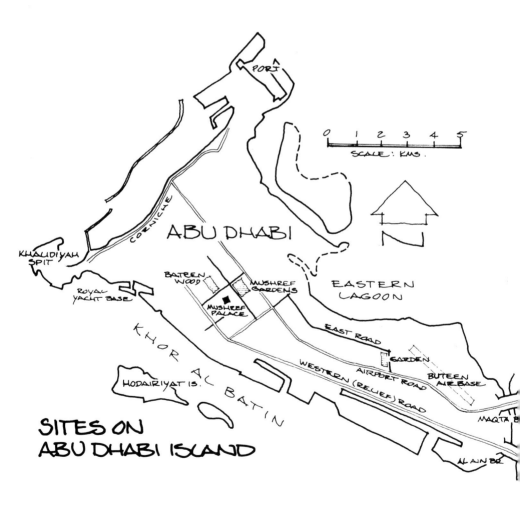

Bateen Wood

Bateen Wood

The natural ground cover on Abu Dhabi island nearly all disappeared during the years of rapid development in the late 1970's, replaced by a network of roads, buildings and other land-use projects. The government gives much priority to tree planting, particularly along roadsides and central reservations, where the linear nature of the habitat suits few birds, except where reservations are wide and undisturbed. The largest and thickest area of trees is Bateen wood, a remarkable area of mixed woodland, much of it dense and in deep shade. Nearly all the trees are drip irrigated, ensuring unhindered growth and attracting large numbers of passerines.

The wood is flanked by Mohammed bin Khalifa Street (near the centre of Abu Dhabi island), adjacent to Mushref Palace. On the lawns in front of Mushref guest palace, about 300 metres from Bateen Wood, numbers of palaearctic waders are likely to be found in autumn. **Ruff** and **Whimbrel** are common in August and September, often joined by **Pacific Golden Plover**, **Common Snipe**, **Curlew**, **Spotted Redshank**, **Redshank**, **Greenshank**, **Green**, **Wood** and **Common Sandpiper**. There are scattered trees, attracting warblers, shrikes

The wood's size is about 25 hectares; not large, but sufficient to provide shelter for a number of species, particulary breeding visitors **Rufous Bush Chat** and **Olivaceous Warbler**, and residents **Collared** and **Palm Dove**, **White-cheeked** and **Red-vented Bulbul**, **Graceful Warbler** and **Purple Sunbird**. The habitat also suits **Grey Francolin**, a recent coloniser whose numbers are currently increasing. Notable migrants recorded in the wood include **Sparrowhawk**, **Wryneck**, **Bluethroat**, **Clamorous Reed Warbler**, **Booted Warbler**, **Ménétries's Warbler**, **Golden Oriole**, **Woodchat** and **Masked Shrike**. A great number of other migrants are likely to occur.

and other passerines. **Lesser**, **Desert Lesser** and **Common Whitethroat** have been recorded here, and pipits and wagtails favour the well-irrigated grass. Flocks of **Common Mynah** regularly feed here, particularly late in the afternoon, and **Bank Mynah** is sometimes found amongst them. The combination of open meadow and adjacent woodland is a successful formula, and can attract a wide selection of migrants, many not listed here, providing a site of great birdwatching interest.

Species recorded in the area include

Cattle Egret	Blue-cheeked Bee-eater	Stonechat	Spotted Flycatcher
Marsh Harrier	European Bee-eater	Isabelline Wheatear	Isabelline Shrike
Steppe Eagle	Hoopoe	Northern Wheatear	Red-backed Shrike
Temminck's Stint	Swallow	Pied Wheatear	Lesser Grey Shrike
Curlew Sandpiper	Tawny Pipit	Rock Thrush	Great Grey Shrike
Turtle Dove	Tree Pipit	Black-throated Thrush	Starling
Rose-ringed Parakeet	Meadow Pipit	Song Thrush	Rose-coloured Starling
Cuckoo	Red-throated Pipit	Blackcap	Pied Mynah
European Nightjar	Water Pipit	Plain Leaf Warbler	Indian Silverbill
Common Swift	Yellow Wagtail	Chiffchaff	Ortolan Bunting
Pallid Swift	Redstart	Willow Warbler	

Al Ain

The garden oasis city of Al Ain has a number of interesting birdwatching sites. The zoo is an obvious choice, its greenery and food handouts attracting many passing migrants. The large animal pens are often circled by **Egyptian Vultures**, scavenging on raw meat fed to the big cats. Many probably nest on neighbouring Jebel Hafit, itself well-worth a visit to observe them soaring over the summit along with **Brown-necked Raven**. The rarer **Lappet-faced Vulture** has nested high up on the 4,000 ft. mountain too. Most other mountain species are represented, including **Desert Lark**, **Pale Crag**

Martin and **Hume's Wheatear**.

The city has a number of parks, the most interesting being Hilli Gardens. The common residents are present, and migrants are also likely to be found. South of Al Ain is Ain al Fayidah, a tourist centre, with ponds and reed beds. **Little Ringed Plover** and **Red-wattled Lapwing** have nested, and a **Black Stork** was reported there in March 1981.

The savannah-type gravel plain about 10 km. north of Al Ain (Al Oha) is favoured by summer visitors **Turtle Dove** and **Yellow-throated Sparrow** which nest in the *Acacia tortilis* trees.

The Liwa oases

Liwa Oasis

The Liwa is reached by travelling south-west from Abu Dhabi for approximately 100 kilometres to Tarif, then a further 100 kilometres south towards the desert interior. The roads are modern and fast. On the latter half of the journey one passes through Medinat Zayed, a quickly developing new town situated amongst the active red sand dunes. Compared to the surrounding desert there *is* some birdlife in the town, though little else than residents **Palm Dove** and **Great Grey Shrike**. However, cultivations and fodder fields along the main road have provided favourable new breeding habitat for an isolated population of **Crested Lark** and summer visitor **Turtle Dove**. The fields attract large numbers of **Black-crowned Finch Lark** and **Hoopoe Lark** in late summer.

Approaching Liwa the sand hills rise to over 100 metres, all showing naturally formed slip faces on the southern side, a result of the prevailing north to north-westerly wind. The oases which run in an east-west arc lie in a chain of depressions linked by a remarkably modern road, a dual-carriageway which runs for 120 kilometres penetrating deep into the remoteness of the region. Drifting sands and high dunes rise on both sides, so venturing off this motorway without a properly equipped vehicle can prove extremely hazardous.

There are 12 permanent villages in the Liwa, situated in the fertile depressions in the northern lee of the dunes. In addition there are 28 settlements, occupied only at date harvest and

pollination time. Few people live away from the village of Liwa (at the main road T-junction, from where the road heads 60 km. east or west). The settlements are no more than simple cultivations seldom larger than 50 hectares, planted predominantly with date palm. There are some other fruit trees, and a mixture of other introduced species, but most importantly fresh water is available, and many cultivations are watered by a series of channels supplied from a diesel pump adjacent to a well.

In spring a good selection of migrants can occur, including **Hoopoe**, **Wryneck**, **Tree Pipit**, **Yellow Wagtail** (of several races), **White Wagtail**, **Redstart**, **Pied Wheatear**, **Semi-collared Flycatcher** and **Pale Rock Sparrow**. The trees often provide shelter for a number of warblers too, amongst which **Olivaceous**, **Ménétries's**, **Desert Lesser Whitethroat**, **Blackcap** and **Willow Warbler** have already been recorded.

Palm Dove are present in all settlements, while **House Sparrow** is quite rare! **Indian Silverbill** is likely to be found in small flocks in even the most remote cultivations, and **Brown-necked Raven** is presen even in the sand dune areas between cultivations. **Great Grey Shrike** is a scarce beeding resident. **Turtle Dove** is an uncommon breeding visitor from late April.

Hirundines of all kind are likely to be found on passage, particularly **Sand Martin** and **Swallow**. Less common **Red-rumped Swallow** and **House Martin** also occur.

CHECKLIST

The common names of all species recorded in the UAE, both wild and feral are listed. Escapees which are considered potential colonisers are included.

The species list follows the order of the book's main text (after voous), and the key to each abbreviated status is as follows. Generally, lower case (rb, pm, etc.) signifies a more scare distribution:

CB – casual breeder
MB – migrant breeder
PM – passage migrant
RB – resident breeder
SV – summer visitor (non-breeding)

WV – winter visitor
V – vagrant
E – escaped or recently introduced
? or ( ) – status uncertain

☐ Little Grebe *Tachybaptus ruficollis*	wv/cb	☐ Spoonbill *Platalea leucorodia*	WV/pm/sv
☐ Great Crested Grebe *Podiceps cristatus*	wv	☐ Greater Flamingo *Phoenicopterus ruber*	WV/SV
☐ Red-necked Grebe *Podiceps grisegena*	V	☐ Mute Swan *Cygnus olor*	V/E
☐ Black-necked Grebe *Podiceps nigricollis*	WV	☐ White-fronted Goose *Anser albifrons*	wv
☐ Jouanin's Petrel *Bulweria fallax*	sv	☐ Greylag Goose *Anser anser*	wv
☐ Flesh-footed Shearwater *Puffinus carneipes*	V/(sv)	☐ Egyptian Goose *Alopochen aegyptiacus*	E
☐ Wedge-tailed Shearwater *Puffinus pacificus*	V	☐ Ruddy Shelduck *Tadorna ferruginea*	V
☐ Audubon's Shearwater *Puffinus lherminieri*	WV	☐ Shelduck *Tadorna tadorna*	pm/wv
☐ Wilson's Storm-Petrel *Oceanites oceanicus*	sv	☐ Cotton Teal *Nettapus coromandelianus*	V
☐ Leach's Storm-Petrel *Oceanodroma leucorhoa*	V	☐ Wigeon *Anas penelope*	wv
☐ Red-billed Tropicbird *Phaethon aethereus*	rb	☐ Gadwall *Anas strepera*	wv
☐ Red-footed Booby *Sula sula*	V	☐ Teal *Anas crecca*	WV/pm
☐ Masked Booby *Sula dactylatra*	V	☐ Mallard *Anas platyrhynchos*	WV/E
☐ Brown Booby *Sula leucogaster*	V	☐ Pintail *Anas acuta*	WV
☐ Great Cormorant *Phalacrocorax carbo*	WV	☐ Garganey *Anas querquedula*	PM
☐ Socotra Cormorant *Phalacrocorax nigrogularis*	RB	☐ Shoveler *Anas clypeata*	WV/PM
☐ White Pelican *Pelecanus onocrotalus*	pm	☐ Marbled Teal *Marmaronetta angustirostris*	V
☐ Dalmatian Pelican *Pelecanus crispus*	V	☐ Red-crested Pochard *Netta rufina*	V
☐ Bittern *Botaurus stellaris*	pm	☐ Pochard *Aythya ferina*	WV
☐ Little Bittern *Ixobrychus minutus*	PM/wv	☐ Ferruginous Duck *Aythya nyroca*	wv
☐ Night Heron *Nycticorax nycticorax*	PM/WV	☐ Tufted Duck *Aythya fuligula*	WV
☐ Little Green Heron *Butorides striatus*	rb	☐ Red-breasted Merganser *Mergus serrator*	V
☐ Squacco Heron *Ardeola ralloides*	pm/wv	☐ Honey Buzzard *Pernis apivorus*	V
☐ Indian Pond Heron *Ardeola grayii*	wv	☐ Black-shouldered Kite *Elanus caeruleus*	V
☐ Cattle Egret *Bubulcus ibis*	pm/wv	☐ Black Kite *Milvus migrans*	pm/wv
☐ Western Reef Heron *Egretta gularis*	RB	☐ Brahminy Kite *Haliastur indus*	V
☐ Little Egret *Egretta garzetta*	PM/WV	☐ Pallas's Fish Eagle *Haliaeetus leucoryphus*	V
☐ Great White Egret *Egretta alba*	WV	☐ Egyptian Vulture *Neophron percnopterus*	RB/pm
☐ Grey Heron *Ardea cinerea*	WV/PM/sv	☐ Griffon Vulture *Gyps fulvus*	wv/pm
☐ Purple Heron *Ardea purpurea*	pm/wv/sv	☐ Lappet-faced Vulture *Torgos tracheliotus*	rb
☐ Black Stork *Ciconia nigra*	V	☐ Short-toed Eagle *Circaetus gallicus*	pm/wv/mb?
☐ White Stork *Ciconia ciconia*	pm	☐ Marsh Harrier *Circus aeruginosus*	WV/pm
☐ Glossy Ibis *Plegadis falcinellus*	pm/wv	☐ Hen Harrier *Circus cyaneus*	pm
☐ Sacred Ibis *Threskiornis aethiopicus*	E?/V?	☐ Pallid Harrier *Circus macrourus*	PM/wv

☐ Montagu's Harrier *Circus pygargus*	pm		☐ Crab Plover *Dromas ardeola*	WV/pm/rb?
☐ Dark Chanting Goshawk *Melierax metabates*	V		☐ Stone Curlew *Burhinus oedicnemus*	pm/wv/E
☐ Goshawk *Accipiter gentilis*	V		☐ Cream-coloured Courser *Cursorius cursor*	rb/pm?
☐ Sparrowhawk *Accipiter nisus*	wv/pm		☐ Collared Pratincole *Glareola pratincola*	PM
☐ Levant Sparrowhawk *Accipiter brevipes*	V		☐ Black-winged Pratincole *Glareola nordmanni*	V
☐ Buzzard *Buteo buteo*	pm/wv		☐ Little Pratincole *Glareola lactea*	V
☐ Long-legged Buzzard *Buteo rufinus*	wv/pm/rb		☐ Little Ringed Plover *Charadrius dubius*	PM/MB
☐ Lesser Spotted Eagle *Aquila pomarina*	V		☐ Ringed Plover *Charadrius hiaticula*	PM/WV/sv
☐ Spotted Eagle *Aquila clanga*	pm/wv		☐ Kentish Plover *Charadrius alexandrinus*	RB/WV/PM
☐ Steppe Eagle *Aquila nipalensis*	PM/wv		☐ Lesser Sand Plover *Charadrius mongolus*	PM/WV/sv
☐ Imperial Eagle *Aquila heliaca*	pm/wv		☐ Greater Sand Plover *Charadrius leschenaultii*	PM/WV
☐ Golden Eagle *Aquila chrysaetos*	rb?		☐ Caspian Plover *Charadrius asiaticus*	pm
☐ Booted Eagle *Hieraaetus pennatus*	pm/wv		☐ Dotterel *Charadrius morinellus*	V
☐ Bonelli's Eagle *Hieraaetus fasciatus*	rb		☐ Pacific Golden Plover *Pluvialis fulva*	WV/PM
☐ Osprey *Pandion haliaetus*	RB/WV		☐ Grey Plover *Pluvialis squatarola*	WV/PM/sv
☐ Lesser Kestrel *Falco naumanni*	pm		☐ Red-wattled Lapwing *Hoplopterus indicus*	rb/pm/mb?
☐ Kestrel *Falco tinnunculus*	WV/PM/rb		☐ Sociable Plover *Chettusia gregaria*	V
☐ Merlin *Falco columbarius*	V		☐ White-tailed Plover *Chettusia leucura*	pm/wv
☐ Hobby *Falco subbuteo*	pm		☐ Lapwing *Vanellus vanellus*	wv
☐ Sooty Falcon *Falco concolor*	mb		☐ Great Knot *Calidris tenuirostris*	V
☐ Lanner Falcon *Falco biarmicus*	E/?		☐ Knot *Calidris canutus*	V
☐ Saker Falcon *Falco cherrug*	E/wv		☐ Sanderling *Calidris alba*	PM/WV/sv
☐ Peregrine Falcon *Falco peregrinus*	E/wv		☐ Little Stint *Calidris minuta*	PM/WV/sv
☐ Barbary Falcon *Falco pelegrinoides*	E/rb?		☐ Temminck's Stint *Calidris temminckii*	PM/wv
☐ Chukar *Alectoris chukar*	E/rb?		☐ Curlew Sandpiper *Calidris ferruginea*	PM/wv/sv
☐ Sand Partridge *Ammoperdix heyi*	RB		☐ Dunlin *Calidris alpina*	WV/PM/sv
☐ Black Francolin *Francolinus francolinus*	E		☐ Broad-billed Sandpiper *Limicola falcinellus*	PM/WV
☐ Grey Francolin *Francolinus pondicerianus*	RB		☐ Ruff *Philomachus pugnax*	PM/wv
☐ Quail *Coturnix coturnix*	pm/E		☐ Jack Snipe *Lymnocryptes minimus*	wv
☐ Water Rail *Rallus aquaticus*	wv		☐ Common Snipe *Gallinago gallinago*	PM/WV
☐ Spotted Crake *Porzana porzana*	PM		☐ Great Snipe *Gallinago media*	pm
☐ Baillon's Crake *Porzana pusilla*	pm		☐ Pintail Snipe *Gallinago stenura*	V
☐ Corncrake *Crex crex*	pm		☐ Woodcock *Scolopax rusticola*	V
☐ Moorhen *Gallinula chloropus*	PM/wv/cb		☐ Black-tailed Godwit *Limosa limosa*	PM/WV
☐ Purple Gallinule *Porphyrio porphyrio*	V		☐ Bar-tailed Godwit *Limosa lapponica*	WV/PM/sv
☐ Coot *Fulica atra*	WV		☐ Whimbrel *Numenius phaeopus*	PM/wv
☐ Common Crane *Grus grus*	V		☐ Curlew *Numenius arquata*	WV/PM/sv
☐ Demoiselle Crane *Anthropoides virgo*	V		☐ Spotted Redshank *Tringa erythropus*	pm/wv
☐ Houbara Bustard *Chlamydotis undulata*	wv		☐ Redshank *Tringa totanus*	WV/PM/sv
☐ Oystercatcher *Haematopus ostralegus*	WV/pm/sv		☐ Marsh Sandpiper *Tringa stagnatilis*	pm/wv
☐ Black-winged Stilt *Himantopus himantopus*	PM/wv/cb		☐ Greenshank *Tringa nebularia*	WV/PM/sv
☐ Avocet *Recurvirostra avosetta*	pm/wv		☐ Green Sandpiper *Tringa ochropus*	PM/WV

☐ Wood Sandpiper *Tringa glareola*	PM/WV	
☐ Terek Sandpiper *Xenus cinereus*	PM/WV	
☐ Common Sandpiper *Actitis hypoleucos*	PM/WV	
☐ Turnstone *Arenaria interpres*	PM/wv	
☐ Red-necked Phalarope *Phalaropus lobatus*	PM/WV	
☐ Grey Phalarope *Phalaropus fulicarius*	wv	
☐ Pomarine Skua *Stercorarius pomarinus*	PM/WV	
☐ Arctic Skua *Stercorarius parasiticus*	PM/wv	
☐ Long-tailed Skua *Stercorarius longicaudus*	V	
☐ Great Skua *Stercorarius skua*	V	
☐ Sooty Gull *Larus hemprichii*	RB/mb/pm	
☐ Great Black-headed Gull *Larus ichthyaetus*	WV/pm	
☐ Black-headed Gull *Larus ridibundus*	WV	
☐ Brown-headed Gull *Larus brunnicephalus*	V or wv?	
☐ Slender-billed Gull *Larus genei*	PM/WV/sv	
☐ Common Gull *Larus canus*	V	
☐ Lesser Black-backed Gull *Larus fuscus*	PM/WV	
☐ Yellow-legged Gull *Larus cachinnans*	PM/WV	
☐ Armenian Gull *Larus armenicus*	WV/PM	
☐ Gull-billed Tern *Gelochelidon nilotica*	PM/wv/sv	
☐ Caspian Tern *Sterna caspia*	wv/pm/rb?	
☐ Swift Tern *Sterna bergii*	MB/wv/rb	
☐ Lesser Crested Tern *Sterna bengalensis*	MB	
☐ Sandwich Tern *Sterna sandvicensis*	PM/WV/SV	
☐ Roseate Tern *Sterna dougallii*	V	
☐ Common Tern *Sterna hirundo*	pm	
☐ White-cheeked Tern *Sterna repressa*	MB	
☐ Bridled Tern *Sterna anaethetus*	MB	
☐ Sooty Tern *Sterna fuscata*	sv	
☐ Little Tern *Sterna albifrons*	pm	
☐ Saunders' Little Tern *Sterna saundersi*	PM/mb	
☐ Whiskered Tern *Chlidonias hybrida*	PM/wv	
☐ White-winged Black Tern *Chlidonias leucopterus*	PM	
☐ Indian Skimmer *Rhynchops albicollis*	V	
☐ Lichtenstein's Sandgrouse *Pterocles lichtensteinii*	RB	
☐ Coronetted Sandgrouse *Pterocles coronatus*	rb?	
☐ Spotted Sandgrouse *Pterocles senegallus*	rb?	
☐ Chestnut-bellied Sandgrouse *Pterocles exustus*	RB	
☐ Black-bellied Sandgrouse *Pterocles orientalus*	E	
☐ Rock Dove *Columba livia*	RB	
☐ Collared Dove *Streptopelia decaocto*	RB/wv	
☐ Turtle Dove *Streptopelia turtur*	PM/mb	

☐ Eastern Turtle Dove *Streptopelia orientalis*	V
☐ Palm Dove *Streptopelia senegalensis*	RB
☐ Namaqua Dove *Oena capensis*	V
☐ Rose-ringed Parakeet *Psittacula krameri*	RB/pm
☐ Alexandrine Parakeet *Psittacula eupatria*	E
☐ Cuckoo *Cuculus canorus*	pm
☐ Indian Koel *Eudynamys scolopacea*	V
☐ Barn Owl *Tyto alba*	rb
☐ Striated Scops Owl *Otus brucei*	mb/rb?
☐ Scops Owl *Otus scops*	PM
☐ Eagle Owl *Bubo bubo*	rb
☐ Little Owl *Athene noctua*	rb
☐ Long-eared Owl *Asio otus*	V
☐ Short-eared Owl *Asio flammeus*	wv
☐ European Nightjar *Caprimulgus europaeus*	PM
☐ Egyptian Nightjar *Caprimulgus aegyptius*	pm
☐ Common Swift *Apus apus*	PM
☐ Pallid Swift *Apus pallidus*	MB/pm
☐ Alpine Swift *Apus melba*	V
☐ Little Swift *Apus affinis*	V
☐ White-collared Kingfisher *Halcyon chloris*	rb
☐ Kingfisher *Alcedo atthis*	WV/PM
☐ Pied Kingfisher *Ceryle rudis*	V/wv?
☐ White-throated Bee-eater *Merops albicollis*	V
☐ Little Green Bee-eater *Merops orientalis*	RB
☐ Blue-cheeked Bee-eater *Merops superciliosus*	PM/mb
☐ European Bee-eater *Merops apiaster*	PM/mb
☐ European Roller *Coracias garrulus*	PM
☐ Indian Roller *Coracias benghalensis*	RB/pm?
☐ Hoopoe *Upupa epops*	PM/wv/mb/rb?
☐ Wryneck *Jynx torquilla*	pm/wv
☐ Black-crowned Finch Lark *Eremopterix nigriceps*	RB
☐ Desert Lark *Ammomanes deserti*	RB
☐ Hoopoe Lark *Alaemon alaudipes*	RB
☐ Bimaculated Lark *Melanocorypha bimaculata*	V
☐ Short-toed Lark *Calandrella brachydactyla*	PM/cb?
☐ Lesser Short-toed Lark *Calandrella rufescens*	pm/wv/mb?
☐ Crested Lark *Galerida cristata*	RB
☐ Skylark *Alauda arvensis*	WV

☐ Temminck's Horned Lark *Eremophila bilopha*	V
☐ Sand Martin *Riparia riparia*	PM/wv
☐ Pale Crag Martin *Hirundo obsoleta*	RB
☐ Crag Martin *Ptyonoprogne rupestris*	pm
☐ Swallow *Hirundo rustica*	PM/cb?
☐ Red-rumped Swallow *Hirundo daurica*	pm
☐ House Martin *Delichon urbica*	pm
☐ Richard's Pipit *Anthus novaeseelandiae*	pm/wv
☐ Tawny Pipit *Anthus campestris*	PM/WV
☐ Long-billed Pipit *Anthus similis*	wv/rb?
☐ Olive-backed Pipit *Anthus hodgsoni*	V
☐ Tree Pipit *Anthus trivialis*	PM
☐ Pechora Pipit *Anthus gustavi*	V
☐ Meadow Pipit *Anthus pratensis*	wv
☐ Red-throated Pipit *Anthus cervinus*	PM/wv
☐ Water Pipit *Anthus spinoletta*	wv
☐ Forest Wagtail *Dendronanthus indicus*	V
☐ Yellow Wagtail *Motacilla flava*	PM/wv
☐ Citrine Wagtail *Motacilla citreola*	pm/wv
☐ Grey Wagtail *Motacilla cinerea*	PM/wv
☐ White Wagtail *Motacilla alba*	WV
☐ White-cheeked Bulbul *Pycnonotus leucogenys*	rb
☐ Yellow-vented Bulbul *Pycnonotus xanthopygos*	RB
☐ Red-whiskered Bulbul *Pycnonotus jocosus*	E
☐ Red-vented Bulbul *Pycnonotus cafer*	RB
☐ Hypocolius *Hypocolius ampelinus*	pm/wv?
☐ Rufous Bush Chat *Cercotrichas galactotes*	pm/mb
☐ Robin *Erithacus rubecula*	wv
☐ Thrush Nightingale *Luscinia luscinia*	pm
☐ Nightingale *Luscinia megarhynchos*	PM
☐ Bluethroat *Luscinia svecica*	WV/PM
☐ White-throated Robin *Irania gutturalis*	pm
☐ Eversmann's Redstart *Phoenicurus erythronotus*	wv
☐ Black Redstart *Phoenicurus ochruros*	WV
☐ Redstart *Phoenicurus phoenicurus*	PM/wv
☐ Whinchat *Saxicola rubetra*	pm
☐ Stonechat *Saxicola torquata*	wv/pm
☐ Isabelline Wheatear *Oenanthe isabellina*	PM/WV
☐ Northern Wheatear *Oenanthe oenanthe*	PM

☐ Pied Wheatear *Oenanthe pleschanka*	PM
☐ Black-eared Wheatear *Oenanthe hispanica*	pm
☐ Desert Wheatear *Oenanthe deserti*	WV/pm
☐ Finsch's Wheatear *Oenanthe finschii*	wv
☐ Red-tailed Wheatear *Oenanthe xanthoprymna*	WV/pm
☐ Eastern Pied Wheatear *Oenanthe picata*	wv/(pm)
☐ Mourning Wheatear *Oenanthe lugens*	wv
☐ Hooded Wheatear *Oenanthe monacha*	wv/rb?
☐ Hume's Wheatear *Oenanthe alboniger*	RB/pm?
☐ White-crowned Black Wheatear *Oenanthe leucopyga*	V
☐ Rock Thrush *Monticola saxatilis*	PM
☐ Blue Rock Thrush *Monticola solitarius*	WV/pm
☐ Ring Ouzel *Turdus torquatus*	V
☐ Blackbird *Turdus merula*	wv
☐ Eye-browed Thrush *Turdus obscurus*	V
☐ Black-throated Thrush *Turdus ruficollis*	wv/pm
☐ Fieldfare *Turdus pilaris*	V
☐ Song Thrush *Turdus philomelos*	WV
☐ Redwing *Turdus iliacus*	V
☐ Mistle Thrush *Turdus viscivorus*	V
☐ Graceful Warbler *Prinia gracilis*	RB
☐ Scrub Warbler *Scotocerca inquieta*	RB
☐ Grasshopper Warbler *Locustella naevia*	pm
☐ Savi's Warbler *Locustella luscinioides*	pm
☐ Moustached Warbler *Acrocephalus melanopogon*	V
☐ Sedge Warbler *Acrocephalus schoenobaenus*	pm
☐ Marsh Warbler *Acrocephalus palustris*	PM
☐ Reed Warbler *Acrocephalus scirpaceus*	PM
☐ Clamorous Reed Warbler *Acrocephalus stentoreus*	PM/wv/rb
☐ Great Reed Warbler *Acrocephalus arundinaceus*	pm
☐ Olivaceous Warbler *Hippolais pallida*	PM/mb
☐ Booted Warbler *Hippolais caligata*	pm/mb?
☐ Upcher's Warbler *Hippolais languida*	pm
☐ Icterine Warbler *Hippolais icterina*	pm
☐ Ménétries's Warbler *Sylvia mystacea*	PM/wv
☐ Desert Warbler *Sylvia nana*	WV
☐ Orphean Warbler *Sylvia hortensis*	pm/wv
☐ Barred Warbler *Sylvia nisoria*	pm
☐ Lesser Whitethroat *Sylvia curruca*	PM

☐ Desert Lesser Whitethroat *Sylvia minula*	WV
☐ Hume's Lesser Whitethroat *Sylvia althaea*	V
☐ Common Whitethroat *Sylvia communis*	PM
☐ Garden Warbler *Sylvia borin*	pm
☐ Blackcap *Sylvia atricapilla*	PM
☐ Yellow-browed Warbler *Phylloscopus inornatus*	pm/wv
☐ Bonelli's Warbler *Phylloscopus bonelli*	V
☐ Wood Warbler *Phylloscopus sibilatrix*	pm
☐ Plain Leaf Warbler *Phylloscopus neglectus*	wv
☐ Chiffchaff *Phylloscopus collybita*	WV/PM
☐ Willow Warbler *Phylloscopus trochilus*	PM
☐ Blue-and-white Flycatcher *Muscicapa cyanomelana*	V
☐ Spotted Flycatcher *Muscicapa striata*	PM
☐ Red-breasted Flycatcher *Ficedula parva*	pm/wv
☐ Semi-collared Flycatcher *Ficedula semitorquata*	pm
☐ Pied Flycatcher *Ficedula hypoleuca*	V
☐ Arabian Babbler *Turdoides squamiceps*	RB
☐ Purple Sunbird *Nectarinia asiatica*	RB
☐ Golden Oriole *Oriolus oriolus*	PM
☐ Isabelline Shrike *Lanius isabellinus*	PM/WV
☐ Red-backed Shrike *Lanius collurio*	PM
☐ Bay-backed Shrike *Lanius vittatus*	V
☐ Lesser Grey Shrike *Lanius minor*	pm
☐ Great Grey Shrike *Lanius excubitor*	RB/PM/wv
☐ Woodchat Shrike *Lanius senator*	PM
☐ Masked Shrike *Lanius nubicus*	pm
☐ House Crow *Corvus splendens*	RB
☐ Brown-necked Raven *Corvus ruficollis*	RB
☐ Starling *Sturnus vulgaris*	WV
☐ Pied Mynah *Sturnus contra*	E
☐ Brahminy Mynah *Sturnus pagodarum*	E
☐ Rose-coloured Starling *Sturnus roseus*	pm
☐ Common Mynah *Acridotheres tristis*	RB/E
☐ Bank Mynah *Acridotheres ginginianus*	rb/E
☐ House Sparrow *Passer domesticus*	RB
☐ Spanish Sparrow *Passer hispaniolensis*	wv
☐ Tree Sparrow *Passer montanus*	V
☐ Pale Rock Sparrow *Petronia brachydactyla*	PM/cb
☐ Yellow-throated Sparrow *Petronia xanthocollis*	MB/pm
☐ Rüppell's Weaver *Ploceus galbula*	E
☐ Masked Weaver *Ploceus intermedius*	E
☐ Red Avadavat *Amandava amandava*	E

☐ Indian Silverbill *Euodice malabarica*	RB/E
☐ Chaffinch *Fringilla coelebs*	V
☐ Brambling *Fringilla montifringilla*	V
☐ Goldfinch *Carduelis carduelis*	V
☐ Siskin *Carduelis spinus*	wv
☐ Linnet *Carduelis cannabina*	V
☐ Trumpeter Finch *Bucanetes githagineus*	wv?/rb?
☐ Common Rosefinch *Carpodacus erythrinus*	pm
☐ Yellowhammer *Emberiza citrinella*	V
☐ House Bunting *Emberiza striolata*	RB
☐ Cinereous Bunting *Emberiza cineracea*	pm
☐ Ortolan Bunting *Emberiza hortulana*	PM
☐ Rustic Bunting *Emberiza rustica*	V
☐ Little Bunting *Emberiza pusilla*	V
☐ Yellow-breasted Bunting *Emberiza aureola*	V
☐ Reed Bunting *Emberiza schoeniclus*	V
☐ Black-headed Bunting *Emberiza melanocephala*	pm/E
☐ Corn Bunting *Miliaria calandra*	wv
☐	
☐	
☐	
☐	
☐	
☐	
☐	
☐	
☐	
☐	

Little Grebe *Tachybaptus ruficollis*

Plate 1

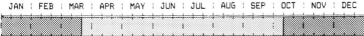

JAN : FEB : MAR : APR : MAY : JUN : JUL : AUG : SEP : OCT : NOV : DEC

Little Grebe

Little Grebe (winter)

Uncommon winter visitor to inland areas of fresh and brackish water with some border growth. Passage from mid September, increasing in October with winter visitors to March. Nests in favoured areas if suitable habitat available, and many winter in breeding areas, including the lower reservoir at Hatta and the recently formed gravel pits at Kalba (although favourable water levels very dependant on annual rainfall). Likely to be found in other sites in late summer following dispersal. – wv/cb

Great Crested Grebe *Podiceps cristatus*

JAN : FEB : MAR : APR : MAY : JUN : JUL : AUG : SEP : OCT : NOV : DEC

Scarce winter visitor to sheltered coasts and creeks, where in November and December single birds have been recorded only half-a-dozen times in recent years. – wv

Red-necked Grebe *Podiceps grisegena*

Vagrant. One reported by several observers on Dubai creek (Khor Dubai) from late December 1984 to early January 1985. Only a handful of accepted records for Arabia. – V

Black-necked Grebe *Podiceps nigricollis*

JAN : FEB : MAR : APR : MAY : JUN : JUL : AUG : SEP : OCT : NOV : DEC

Regular and fairly common winter visitor. Most occur from mid September to February, occasionally to March. Small numbers of prospective breeders may remain to May or June, though nests have not yet been found. Favours irrigation ponds, reservoirs, sewage treatment plants and decorative lakes with sufficient border vegetation. Sometimes in small flocks in favoured locations. Often reluctant to fly, allowing close observation. A casual breeder in Qatar and in Oman (suspected 1989). – WV

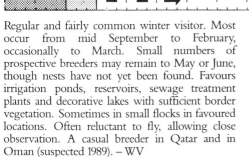

Black-necked Grebe (non-breeding)

Jouanin's Petrel *Bulweria fallax*

JAN	FEB	MAR	APR	MAY	JUN	JUL	AUG	SEP	OCT	NOV	DEC

Scarce visitor to feeding areas along the edge of the continental shelf in the Gulf of Oman. Strays (mainly non-breeding birds) have been reported off the East Coast at all times of the year. However most records coincide with the SW monsoon from late summer to November, when it has been seen at fish shoals close to the shore. Evidence suggests breeding areas include the interior of the southern Arabian desert. Majority appear to move south about the end of November, returning in March. – sv

Note: Many reports confused with Wedge-tailed Shearwater *Puffinus pacificus* of which there are few accepted records (see below).

Flesh-footed Shearwater *Puffinus carneipes*

A rare visitor from Australasian breeding grounds, it occurs far offshore in the Gulf of Oman, feeding at the edge of the continental shelf. A summer visitor to the Arabian Sea, though more likely to occur in the Gulf of Oman during the end of the south-west monsoon in December, when it has been recorded off the East Coast. – V/(sv)

Wedge-tailed Shearwater *Puffinus pacificus*

Rare summer visitor to the Arabian Sea, some likely to occur far offshore in the Gulf of Oman. Widely dispersed pelagic species which roams the Indian and Pacific Oceans straying occasionally to the northern tip of the continental shelf, in UAE waters, where it feeds on food generated from upwellings associated with the south-west monsoon. Non-breeding birds can occur at other times. Likely to be confused with Jouanin's Petrel, and lack of experienced observers offshore probably accounts for lack of records. No records yet for the Arabian Gulf. – V

Audubon's Shearwater *Puffinus lherminieri*

JAN	FEB	MAR	APR	MAY	JUN	JUL	AUG	SEP	OCT	NOV	DEC

Flocks of several hundred of the race *P. l. persicus* (Persian Shearwater) occur regularly from August in the Gulf of Oman and Straits of Hormuz, with small numbers wintering inside the Arabian Gulf from September to April. Some are present throughout the year although most have departed for breeding areas by May. (A colony exists on the Kuria Muria Islands off southern Oman and nesting areas off Musandam may yet be discovered). – WV

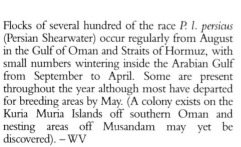

Wilson's Storm-Petrel *Oceanites oceanicus*

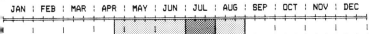

JAN	FEB	MAR	APR	MAY	JUN	JUL	AUG	SEP	OCT	NOV	DEC

Regular non-breeding visitor, most present late April to August and occasionally at other times. Likely to occur in numbers along the edge of the continental shelf in the Arabian Sea in mid summer, when some also reported inside the Arabian Gulf. It breeds in the Antarctic region during the southern summer. – sv

Leach's Storm-Petrel *Oceanodroma leucorhoa*

Vagrant, one found dying at the old Sharjah airfield on 8th June 1969, the Gulf's only record. – V

Red-billed Tropicbird *Phaethon aethereus*   Plate 1

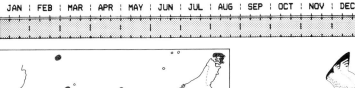

JAN	FEB	MAR	APR	MAY	JUN	JUL	AUG	SEP	OCT	NOV	DEC

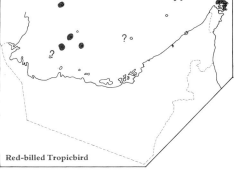

Red-billed Tropicbird

Resident and dispersive. Coastal sightings are rare, and only likely to be found flying far offshore where it is usually solitary. It nests colonially in holes on rocky islets in the Arabian Gulf and on coastal cliffs on the Musandam peninsula. Breeding season appears to vary with location (and food availability) but birds have been recorded at nest sites from the end of October, with eggs from early December. Breeding activity continues until mid May, when most birds disperse, though young may still be in the nest in June at some colonies. Adults circle nest sites in noisy chasing flocks morning and late afternoon. – rb

Red-footed Booby *Sula sula*

An unusual record of one remaining on board a northbound ship at sea through UAE waters in the Gulf of Oman in late August 1979. Breeds in tropical oceans, and occurs as a vagrant in the Arabian Sea. Normal range includes the southern Indian Ocean. – V

Masked Booby *Sula dactylatra*

One north of Ras al Khaimah in May 1973 and one juvenile 19th May 1988 offshore Abu Dhabi. Otherwise unknown inside Arabian Gulf. Breeds in large numbers on Kuria Muria Islands off southern Oman, though only occasionally seen as far north as the Straits of Hormuz, and usually well offshore. – V

Brown Booby *Sula leucogaster*

Vagrant. Less than a handful of reports, including one adult at an oil installation offshore Sharjah late October 1986. Also reported mid January and spring. Might wander from breeding grounds in the Red Sea and Gulf of Aden to the Gulf of Oman. Care should be taken not to confuse it with juvenile Masked Booby. – V

Great Cormorant *Phalacrocorax carbo*

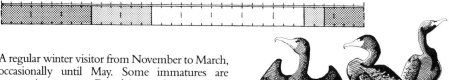

A regular winter visitor from November to March, occasionally until May. Some immatures are present in summer. Found in good numbers on sandbanks, lagoons, coastal breakwaters and occasionally at inland lakes. Care should be taken not to confuse it with the locally abundant Socotra Cormorant, which is generally not found inland. – WV

Socotra Cormorant *Phalacrocorax nigrogularis*   Plate 1

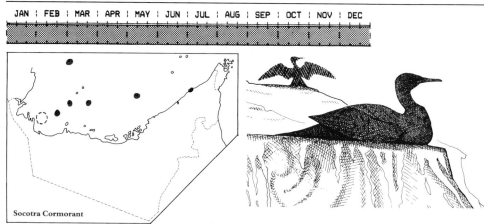

Socotra Cormorant

Abundant breeding resident found in extraordinary numbers just offshore and in some coastal lagoons. Many thousands can be observed flying in long extended V-formation at wave height, believed to be feeding sorties, although the reasons for its massive movements are not fully understood. Nests in large colonies on some Gulf islands between September and February, with the actual laying period dependent upon food availability. Often perches on breakwaters, harbour walls and buoys. Adults not found inland, though immatures have been observed straying to ponds short distances from the coast.

Numbers may have decreased in recent years as a result of disturbance on their island breeding sites, which need protection. – RB

White Pelican *Pelecanus onocrotalus*

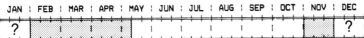

JAN	FEB	MAR	APR	MAY	JUN	JUL	AUG	SEP	OCT	NOV	DEC

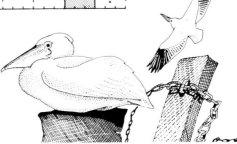

Very scarce passage migrant, reported February to May, and November, mainly along coasts. Breeding areas include the upper Euphrates and the low-lying basins of Uzbekistan, although drainage projects have reduced its range. – pm

Dalmatian Pelican *Pelecanus crispus*

Vagrant. One at Abu Dhabi 16th December 1970, and one landed on a Gulf oil installation on 19th January 1980. Nearest regular wintering grounds include the Iraqi marshes and the Gulf coast of Iran. – V

Bittern *Botaurus stellaris*

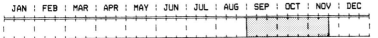

JAN	FEB	MAR	APR	MAY	JUN	JUL	AUG	SEP	OCT	NOV	DEC

Scarce autumn passage migrant, most recorded in September, occasionally to mid November. Usually near water with shaded cover and good border vegetation. Care should be taken not to confuse it with immature Night Heron, which is widespread at this time. – pm

Little Bittern *Ixobrychus minutus*

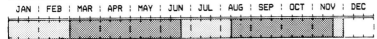

JAN	FEB	MAR	APR	MAY	JUN	JUL	AUG	SEP	OCT	NOV	DEC

Fairly common passage migrant which has occurred in all months, though more regularly March to mid June and August to November. Skulks in cover around fresh or brackish ponds, sometimes perching in trees. Immatures more frequent. Breeds in southern Oman, eastern Saudi Arabia and has bred in Bahrain, although main nesting range is further north, extending from mainland Europe to central Asia. – PM/wv.

Night Heron *Nycticorax nycticorax* — Plate 1

JAN	FEB	MAR	APR	MAY	JUN	JUL	AUG	SEP	OCT	NOV	DEC

Common passage migrant and winter visitor September to April, particularly frequent in autumn. Occasionally summer months. Immatures more common, and may occur in flocks of twenty or more on migration. Found at fresh and brackish water, irrigation ponds and open sewage works where roosting cover is available. Also occurs in wet wadis on passage. – PM/WV.

Immature Night Heron

Little Green Heron *Butorides striatus* — Plate 2

JAN	FEB	MAR	APR	MAY	JUN	JUL	AUG	SEP	OCT	NOV	DEC

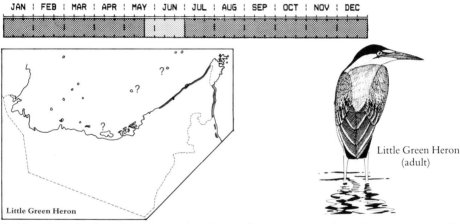

Little Green Heron

Little Green Heron (adult)

Resident. Recently adapted to a man-made habitat, feeding from harbour walls, breakwaters and shaded jetties, in addition to its traditionally favoured mangroves. Fishes from shady rocks near the waterline. Also favours water-filled rubbish dumps, sewage disposal sites and gravel pits. Nesting recorded March to July, in mangroves or rock cavities. In autumn also found in small numbers at ponds and lakes with border cover. – rb

Squacco Heron *Ardeola ralloides*

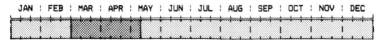

JAN	FEB	MAR	APR	MAY	JUN	JUL	AUG	SEP	OCT	NOV	DEC

Uncommon visitor from discontinuous breeding areas across southern Europe and western Asia. Occurs in the Arabian Gulf in all months but more regularly March to early May. Frequents irrigated open parkland, and marshy ponds with cover. Care should be taken not to confuse it with the darker-backed Indian Pond Heron, an occasional winter visitor to East Coast mangroves. – pm/wv

Indian Pond Heron *Ardeola grayii*

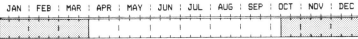

JAN	FEB	MAR	APR	MAY	JUN	JUL	AUG	SEP	OCT	NOV	DEC

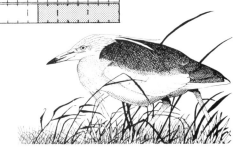

Uncommon and localised winter visitor, particularly to East Coast mangroves. Reported in all months from September to May, but suspect some may be mistaken *A. ralloides*, including reports from Arabian Gulf coast. Most confirmed records mid October to March. Usually occurs singly, and is often inactive. – wv

Cattle Egret *Bubulcus ibis*

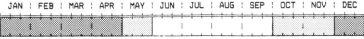

JAN	FEB	MAR	APR	MAY	JUN	JUL	AUG	SEP	OCT	NOV	DEC

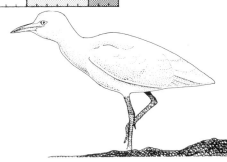

Fairly erratic autumn migrant and late winter visitor, though numbers quite variable. Most occur from December to late April at inland marshes and sewage works. Passage October, November, April and May. Becoming more common with increase in grassed landscaped areas and meadows. Sometimes on creeks, though rarely on coasts. Acquires orange neck and head plumes in early April. – pm/wv

Western Reef Heron *Egretta gularis*   Plate 2

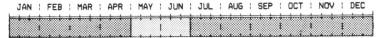

JAN	FEB	MAR	APR	MAY	JUN	JUL	AUG	SEP	OCT	NOV	DEC

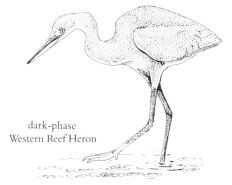

dark-phase
Western Reef Heron

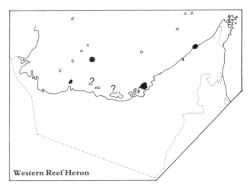

Western Reef Heron

Resident and common at most times of the year, breeding from April to June in mangroves and on some islands. A familiar sight on creeks and mudflats from July to April, where it is an active feeder in the shallows. Present in white and dark phases. The predominant dark-grey phase is unmistakable. White-phase can be confusing, but usually separated from Little Egret by having a stouter, paler bill and more yellow around the lower legs. – RB

Little Egret *Egretta garzetta*

JAN	FEB	MAR	APR	MAY	JUN	JUL	AUG	SEP	OCT	NOV	DEC

Regular passage migrant and winter visitor in small numbers. More likely to be found away from coastal sites, hunting around shallow freshwater ponds, marshes and creeks. Generally common from September to March, but may occur at other times, though scarce after May. Separated from white-phase Western Reef Heron by its finer all-black bill and distinctive yellow/green feet. – PM/WV

Great White Egret *Egretta alba*

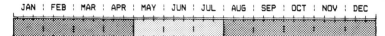

JAN	FEB	MAR	APR	MAY	JUN	JUL	AUG	SEP	OCT	NOV	DEC

Common non-breeding visitor from August to April. Favours khors, marshes, lakes and other large inland areas of shallow water with fish. Occasionally seen in loose groups, though can occur singly amongst other herons. Some non-breeding birds present in summer. Smaller eastern sub-species *E. a. modesta* often occurs. – WV

Grey Heron *Ardea cinerea*

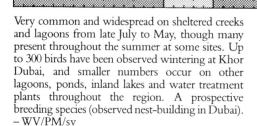

JAN	FEB	MAR	APR	MAY	JUN	JUL	AUG	SEP	OCT	NOV	DEC

Very common and widespread on sheltered creeks and lagoons from late July to May, though many present throughout the summer at some sites. Up to 300 birds have been observed wintering at Khor Dubai, and smaller numbers occur on other lagoons, ponds, inland lakes and water treatment plants throughout the region. A prospective breeding species (observed nest-building in Dubai). – WV/PM/sv

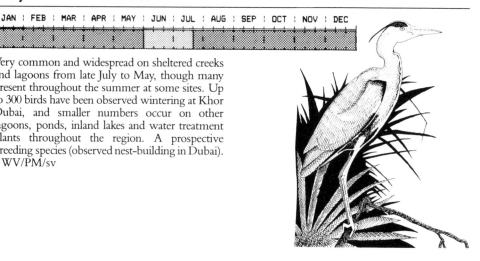

Purple Heron *Ardea purpurea* — Plate 2

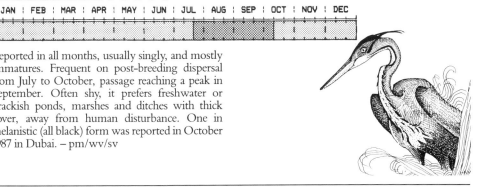

| JAN | FEB | MAR | APR | MAY | JUN | JUL | AUG | SEP | OCT | NOV | DEC |

Reported in all months, usually singly, and mostly immatures. Frequent on post-breeding dispersal from July to October, passage reaching a peak in September. Often shy, it prefers freshwater or brackish ponds, marshes and ditches with thick cover, away from human disturbance. One in melanistic (all black) form was reported in October 1987 in Dubai. – pm/wv/sv

Black Stork *Ciconia nigra*

Rare passage migrant. A handful of records in March, April and September in Abu Dhabi and surrounding areas. Many winter in southern Iran, Pakistan and northern India, where it favours marshes and river meadows. – V

White Stork *Ciconia ciconia* — Plate 2

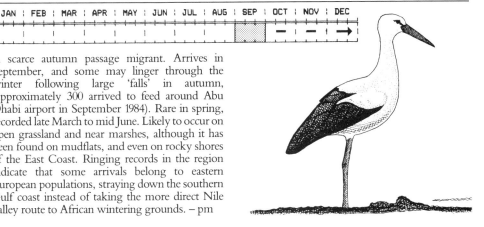

| JAN | FEB | MAR | APR | MAY | JUN | JUL | AUG | SEP | OCT | NOV | DEC |

A scarce autumn passage migrant. Arrives in September, and some may linger through the winter following large 'falls' in autumn, (approximately 300 arrived to feed around Abu Dhabi airport in September 1984). Rare in spring, recorded late March to mid June. Likely to occur on open grassland and near marshes, although it has been found on mudflats, and even on rocky shores of the East Coast. Ringing records in the region indicate that some arrivals belong to eastern European populations, straying down the southern Gulf coast instead of taking the more direct Nile valley route to African wintering grounds. – pm

Glossy Ibis *Plegadis falcinellus* — Plate 2

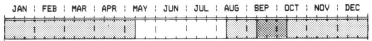

| JAN | FEB | MAR | APR | MAY | JUN | JUL | AUG | SEP | OCT | NOV | DEC |

Regular on autumn passage, mid September to early October, though never common. Very irregular at other times and individuals may occur in all months August to early May. Overwintering reported mid October to late March. Favours fresh or brackish marshes, sewage works and irrigated grassland. Can be quite approachable, although its glossy plumage is not apparent in autumn, even at close range. Breeds in discontinuous areas from Europe to Asia. – pm/wv

Spoonbill *Platalea leucorodia*

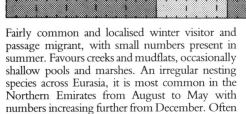

| JAN | FEB | MAR | APR | MAY | JUN | JUL | AUG | SEP | OCT | NOV | DEC |

Fairly common and localised winter visitor and passage migrant, with small numbers present in summer. Favours creeks and mudflats, occasionally shallow pools and marshes. An irregular nesting species across Eurasia, it is most common in the Northern Emirates from August to May with numbers increasing further from December. Often rests during the heat of the day, before feeding at dusk. – WV/pm/sv

Greater Flamingo *Phoenicopterus ruber*   Plate 3

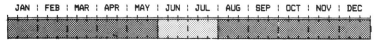

| JAN | FEB | MAR | APR | MAY | JUN | JUL | AUG | SEP | OCT | NOV | DEC |

Common and localised winter visitor to large lagoons and mudflats mostly on the Gulf coast. Some present, mainly immatures, at all times of the year. Extremely sensitive to disturbance it is easily displaced, and nesting conditions are few worldwide. It is most common at Khor Dubai, where several hundred are protected by the Dubai Government, following the creation of an island 'nest' site. Last recorded breeding in the Gulf, near Kuwait in 1926. – WV/SV
Note: Recoveries in the region indicate that many birds are from Central Asian colonies at Lake Rezaiyeh and Azerbaijan.

Mute Swan *Cygnus olor*

Winter vagrant, three recorded 13th December 1984 in Abu Dhabi (reported mid December 1984 in Bahrain). Escapes also likely from local free-flying collections. – V/E

White-fronted Goose *Anser albifrons*

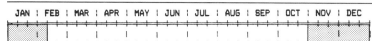

| JAN | FEB | MAR | APR | MAY | JUN | JUL | AUG | SEP | OCT | NOV | DEC |

Scarce and irregular winter visitor from early November to early February. Small flocks can occur on damp grassland, water treatment plants and areas of fresh and brackish water near suitable grazing. Seen in flight near coasts and offshore islands on passage. Eurasian pink-billed race *A. a. albifrons* occurs. – wv

Greylag Goose *Anser anser* Plate 3

JAN	FEB	MAR	APR	MAY	JUN	JUL	AUG	SEP	OCT	NOV	DEC

Uncommon winter visitor from November to mid March. Likely to be found at wetland areas including water treatment plants, marshes and ponds with nearby grazing. Occurs less frequently on creeks and lagoons. Currently extending its wintering quarters as suitable habitat becomes more widely available in the Gulf. The Asian race *A. a. rubirostris*, with pink legs and bill, is regularly recorded. – wv

Ruddy Shelduck *Tadorna ferruginea*

Rare winter visitor, a handful of records October to January in Dubai and Abu Dhabi, mostly small groups. Once in summer 1982 at Abu Dhabi. May be more frequent than records indicate. Prefers freshwater marshes, coastal creeks and mudflats. – V

Shelduck *Tadorna tadorna*

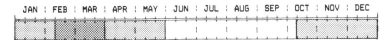

JAN	FEB	MAR	APR	MAY	JUN	JUL	AUG	SEP	OCT	NOV	DEC

Scarce and irregular winter visitor and passage migrant usually occurring singly or in small groups. Found on tidal creek edges, brackish and freshwater pools, water treatment plants and inland ponds from mid October to May. Regular from mid February to March and passage recorded in April and May. – pm/wv

Cotton Teal *Nettapus coromandelianus*

Vagrant and dispersive from its origins on the Indian sub-continent. One recorded in Dubai in early November 1984, and a small number were present at Hatta reservoir in February 1985. Winters annually in Oman. – V

Wigeon *Anas penelope*

JAN	FEB	MAR	APR	MAY	JUN	JUL	AUG	SEP	OCT	NOV	DEC

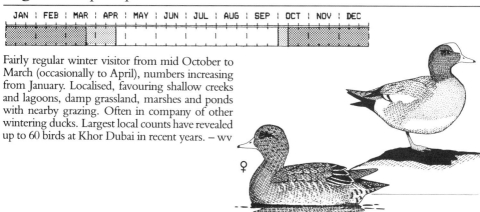

Fairly regular winter visitor from mid October to March (occasionally to April), numbers increasing from January. Localised, favouring shallow creeks and lagoons, damp grassland, marshes and ponds with nearby grazing. Often in company of other wintering ducks. Largest local counts have revealed up to 60 birds at Khor Dubai in recent years. – wv

Gadwall *Anas strepera*

JAN	FEB	MAR	APR	MAY	JUN	JUL	AUG	SEP	OCT	NOV	DEC

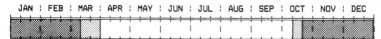

Present in small numbers from mid October (rarely from early September) to late March on ponds, reservoirs, water treatment plants and brackish marshes. Regularly occurs in the Northern Emirates, where numbers increase slightly from January. Breeds throughout central Asia near fresh water with rank vegetation. – wv

Teal *Anas crecca*

JAN	FEB	MAR	APR	MAY	JUN	JUL	AUG	SEP	OCT	NOV	DEC

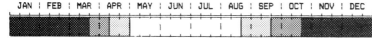

Very common and widespread from September to April, with numbers peaking from late October to mid March. Found on fresh or brackish inland ponds, lakes, marshes and standing water. Can be seen in flocks of several hundred in mid winter. Less frequently on tidal creeks and lagoons. Eclipse plumaged birds can be confused with Garganey in autumn. – WV/pm

Mallard *Anas platyrhynchos* | Plate 3

| JAN | FEB | MAR | APR | MAY | JUN | JUL | AUG | SEP | OCT | NOV | DEC |

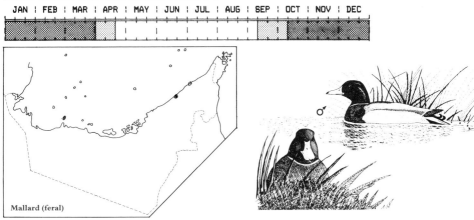

Mallard (feral)

A common winter visitor from October to late March, and occasionally at other times. Favoured haunts include ponds, reservoirs, creeks, lagoons and water treatment plants. Several hundred have wintered on Khor Dubai in recent years. Its status is obscured by the existence of introduced flocks, which breed in early spring (chicks present from late March). – WV/E

Pintail *Anas acuta*

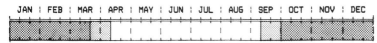

| JAN | FEB | MAR | APR | MAY | JUN | JUL | AUG | SEP | OCT | NOV | DEC |

Common winter visitor from sub-Arctic breeding grounds, arriving in early October (occasionally September) departing mid March, with stragglers present until April. Usually restless and shy, it rarely remains in one wintering site. Found on tidal lagoons, fresh and brackish inland ponds and water treatment plants. Some remain in eclipse plumage until December. – WV

Garganey *Anas querquedula*

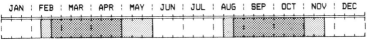

| JAN | FEB | MAR | APR | MAY | JUN | JUL | AUG | SEP | OCT | NOV | DEC |

Common passage migrant. Main autumn passage late August to October (fewer to mid November). Some strays occasionally in winter, though most reports show confusion with *A. crecca*. Northerly passage noted mid February to April, continuing to May some years when most other ducks have departed. Found on creeks and areas of shallow fresh and brackish water, even quite small ponds and flooded areas. – PM

Shoveler *Anas clypeata*

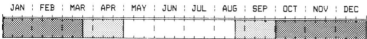

| JAN | FEB | MAR | APR | MAY | JUN | JUL | AUG | SEP | OCT | NOV | DEC |

Common, though localised winter visitor and passage migrant. Autumn passage can occur from late August, though more likely from October, wintering to mid March. Some may linger to late April, and has been recorded in June. Found on shallow coastal creeks, lagoons, inland ponds, marshes and reservoirs. Occurs in flocks of 50 or more in favoured locations, mostly Northern Emirates. – WV/PM

Marbled Teal *Marmaronetta angustirostris*

Vagrant from breeding sites scattered across the warm temperate zone, where it usually disperses locally following breeding. Two at Dhayah (north of Ras al Khaimah) in October 1975, and 25 at Abu Dhabi on 1st March 1972. No acceptable recent records. In winter it generally favours shallow pools with surrounding vegetation. – V

Red-crested Pochard *Netta rufina*

Vagrant, or very scarce winter visitor, most records in December. Will occur on brackish or freshwater ponds and marshes, less likely on creeks and lagoons. – V

Pochard *Aythya ferina*

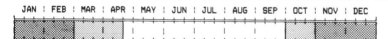

| JAN | FEB | MAR | APR | MAY | JUN | JUL | AUG | SEP | OCT | NOV | DEC |

Regular, though localised winter visitor, often in the company of Tufted and Ferruginous Duck. Present from October to February, occasionally to mid April (rarely to June). Prefers freshwater ponds, marshes and reservoirs, mostly in Northern Emirates. Flocks are often reluctant to fly and usually overwinter at one site until spring. – WV

Ferruginous Duck *Aythya nyroca*

Plate 3

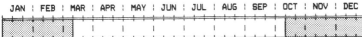

| JAN | FEB | MAR | APR | MAY | JUN | JUL | AUG | SEP | OCT | NOV | DEC |

Scarcer than Pochard, recorded irregularly and in small numbers, (usually less than five together) from mid October to February on fresh or brackish ponds, reservoirs and at water treatment plants. Occasionally to early March. Sometimes on sheltered coastal creeks and lagoons. – wv

Tufted Duck *Aythya fuligula*

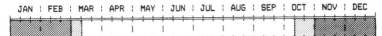

| JAN | FEB | MAR | APR | MAY | JUN | JUL | AUG | SEP | OCT | NOV | DEC |

Fairly regular winter visitor, though quite localised, and usually only on creeks, ponds, lagoons and reservoirs in the Northern Emirates. Most arrivals recorded from early November (occasionally from mid October); remaining in one site until early March often in small flocks with Pochard. - WV

Red-breasted Merganser *Mergus serrator*

Vagrant to Arabian Gulf region, and only two reports in recent times in the UAE. One observed near islands west of Abu Dhabi late October 1972, and a mobile flock of up to 15 apparently at home in shallow lagoons on the Gulf coast between Umm al Quwain and Ras al Khaimah late November to December 1988. – V

Honey Buzzard *Pernis apivorus*

Rare. Less than a handful of recent records, spanning September to February with most occuring in Abu Dhabi. Pale adults and some juveniles can be difficult to separate from more commonly occuring Long-legged Buzzard *Buteo rufinus*. – V

Black-shouldered Kite *Elanus caeruleus* Plate 3

One female recorded in southern suburbs of Dubai on 24th February 1984, the only current record for the Gulf states. Arabian breeding grounds lie within North and South Yemen, where it is localised and usually resident, although individuals are known to wander. – V

Black Kite *Milvus migrans*

One of the world's most numerous birds of prey, though scarce in the Emirates, where it is reported only in small numbers in spring and autumn, and less frequently at other times. Found scavenging at rubbish dumps or along the coast feeding on discarded fish. Breeds across the Eurasian landmass, most wintering in Africa. – pm/wv
Note: Some immature birds may be mistaken for Red Kite *M. milvus* (not known in the UAE).

Brahminy Kite *Haliastur indus*

Single birds recorded April and October 1986, and two from December 1986 to the end of January 1987 in Dubai. Probable true vagrants, though some doubts about their origin still remain. – V

Pallas's Fish Eagle *Haliaeetus leucoryphus*

Vagrant. One recorded at Ras al Khaimah 29th October 1972. Nearest regular wintering grounds are in Pakistan and India. – V

Egyptian Vulture *Neophron percnopterus*

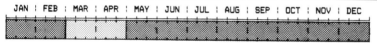

A local resident of the mountains, though rarely north of Masafi. The commonest vulture and usually only observed soaring. Nests February to April. Occasionally recorded in other areas in late autumn and winter, including the Arabian Gulf coast. Often congregates at carrion and rubbish dumps, and may be seen regularly over Al Ain zoo and at the top of Jebel Hafit, a traditional nesting site. – RB/pm

Griffon Vulture *Gyps fulvus*

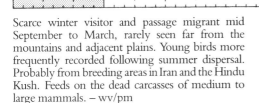

JAN	FEB	MAR	APR	MAY	JUN	JUL	AUG	SEP	OCT	NOV	DEC

Scarce winter visitor and passage migrant mid September to March, rarely seen far from the mountains and adjacent plains. Young birds more frequently recorded following summer dispersal. Probably from breeding areas in Iran and the Hindu Kush. Feeds on the dead carcasses of medium to large mammals. – wv/pm

Note: Movements of large vultures are not well known and many are misidenitified. Sightings are infrequent as they soar at great height (10,000 feet or more) and cover great distances.

Lappet-faced Vulture *Torgos tracheliotus*

JAN	FEB	MAR	APR	MAY	JUN	JUL	AUG	SEP	OCT	NOV	DEC

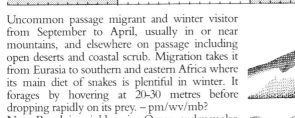

Lappet-faced Vulture

Localised breeding resident of mountains and rocky outcrops, recorded soaring over foothills and associated gravel plains, particularly in late autumn and winter months. Darker form occurs, and some mistakenly reported as Black Vulture (whose status is unclear – see page 168). Soars for long periods at great height, usually with its mate. The large untidy stick nest is built from December on a mountain ledge or tree top. It dominates other vultures at a carcass. – rb

Short-toed Eagle *Circaetus gallicus*

JAN	FEB	MAR	APR	MAY	JUN	JUL	AUG	SEP	OCT	NOV	DEC

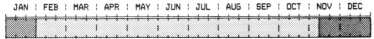

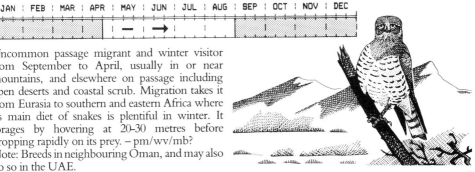

Uncommon passage migrant and winter visitor from September to April, usually in or near mountains, and elsewhere on passage including open deserts and coastal scrub. Migration takes it from Eurasia to southern and eastern Africa where its main diet of snakes is plentiful in winter. It forages by hovering at 20-30 metres before dropping rapidly on its prey. – pm/wv/mb?
Note: Breeds in neighbouring Oman, and may also do so in the UAE.

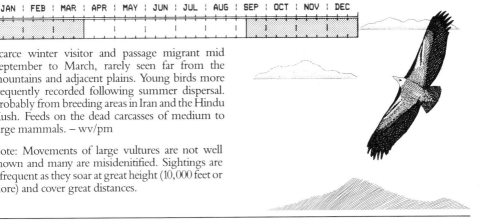

Marsh Harrier *Circus aeruginosus*

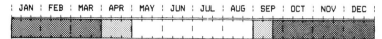

JAN	FEB	MAR	APR	MAY	JUN	JUL	AUG	SEP	OCT	NOV	DEC

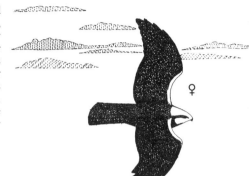

Common and widespread winter visitor and passage migrant favouring coastal creeks, mudflats, sewage dumps and mangrove swamps. Generally present from October to March, though one or two likely at other times. Immatures and females more common as many adult males remain near northern breeding areas. Flies low and appears suddenly to surprise its prey, which include birds, rodents and even fish. Widespread from Europe across the USSR to the Pacific coast, wherever there are lakes, marshes and rivers. – WV/pm

Hen Harrier *Circus cyaneus*

Scarce passage migrant. The rarest harrier, very few adult males recorded, and exact status obscured by largely unidentified female and immature birds (sometimes called 'ring-tailed' harriers) reported in spring and autumn. Favours open country and coastal dunes. – pm

Pallid Harrier *Circus macrourus*

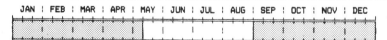

JAN	FEB	MAR	APR	MAY	JUN	JUL	AUG	SEP	OCT	NOV	DEC

Regular passage migrant and winter visitor in small numbers September to March, sometimes common in October, occasionally to May. Adult males infrequent, and females and immatures require careful identification (face-pattern diagnostic). Seen in dry open country, gravel plains and rolling semi-desert areas. Prey consists mostly of small rodents. Breeds on the Russian steppes. – PM/wv

Montagu's Harrier *Circus pygargus*

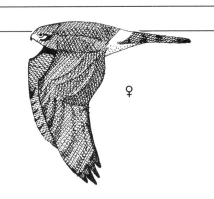

Very scarce passage migrant, and possible winter visitor. Status based on adult males sighted, November, March and April. Probably occurs from September but reports highlight identification difficulties, as confusion is likely with female and immature Pallid Harriers. Favours cultivations, irrigated fields and marshier areas than Pallid Harrier. – pm

Dark Chanting Goshawk *Melierax metabates*

Vagrant. One found on Dalma Island (and subsequently trapped and caged) in February 1989. One, whose origins are still unknown, was seen in Abu Dhabi on 15th April 1988, possibly also a wild bird. Nearest breeding grounds are South Yemen and the south-west Arabian peninsula, where it is usually resident, though such erratic dispersal is regularly reported. – V

Goshawk *Accipiter gentilis*

Vagrant or rare winter visitor. Reported infrequently October to April. Favours woods adjacent to open country. Comparable size of female Sparrowhawk can cause confusion with male Goshawk. – V

Sparrowhawk *Accipiter nisus*

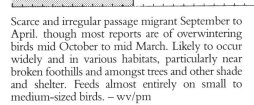

Scarce and irregular passage migrant September to April. though most reports are of overwintering birds mid October to mid March. Likely to occur widely and in various habitats, particularly near broken foothills and amongst trees and other shade and shelter. Feeds almost entirely on small to medium-sized birds. – wv/pm

Levant Sparrowhawk *Accipiter brevipes*

One female reported at Dhaid (50 km. inland from Sharjah) late October 1977 probably this species. Generally very rare in Arabia. Some other reports do not satisfactorily rule out Sparrowhawk *A. nisus*. – V

Buzzard *Buteo buteo*

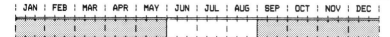

| JAN | FEB | MAR | APR | MAY | JUN | JUL | AUG | SEP | OCT | NOV | DEC |

Scarce passage migrant, some in winter. Most appear to pass through western Arabia on a broad front, and only relatively small numbers are recorded in the UAE. Eastern race *B.b. vulpinus* (Steppe Buzzard) is prevalent. Recorded September to May, though may occur in small parties at favoured locations (over cultivations) November to February. Similar to Long-legged Buzzard, with which it is sometimes confused. Hunts mainly from a perch, preying on rodents and lizards, or carrion if available. – pm/wv

Long-legged Buzzard *Buteo rufinus*

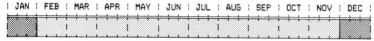

| JAN | FEB | MAR | APR | MAY | JUN | JUL | AUG | SEP | OCT | NOV | DEC |

Long-legged Buzzard

Uncommon winter visitor and passage migrant, with small numbers probably resident. Occurs over hills, outcrops, open plains and cultivations. Has been seen at all times of the year, and migrants are commonly recorded from September to April. Reported to nest in the mountains from February, with eggs in March. Preys on mammals, lizards and medium sized birds. Might be initially confused with other buzzards, though this species' larger size and more rufous plumage aids its identification. – wv/pm/rb

Spotted Eagle *Aquila clanga*

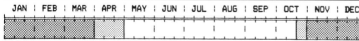

| JAN | FEB | MAR | APR | MAY | JUN | JUL | AUG | SEP | OCT | NOV | DEC |

Regular autumn and winter visitor from nesting grounds in the northern Soviet forests. Found in small numbers from late October to April. Most are present from November to March, wintering at favoured coastal locations, including mangroves, marshes, inshore islands, lagoons and mudflats, though some also occur further inland on passage. – pm/wv

Lesser Spotted Eagle *Aquila pomarina*

Vagrant, though probably occurs more regularly than reports indicate. First confirmed record, of one immature bird at Zabeel water treatment plant in late February 1990. Difficulty in separating this species from some other *Aquila* eagles has clouded many records. Rare migrant in Oman, most recorded October to March. – V

Steppe Eagle *Aquila nipalensis*

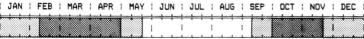

Fairly common and regular passage migrant from September to November and mid February to mid May, with a few overwintering. Found in open areas with scattered trees, semi-desert and gravel plains, and rarely far from water. Breeds from the Ukraine to Manchuria, and from south-east Iran to Burma in areas of open grassland and savannah. Prey includes rodents, lizards and insects, and will feed on carrion and at rubbish dumps. As with most large raptors it is often persecuted. – PM/wv

Imperial Eagle *Aquila heliaca*

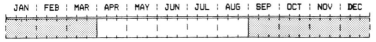

Scarce passage migrant recorded in ones and twos (often family groups) September (occasionally from August) to March in open country with scattered trees, often near wet areas. Soars to great height, before gliding and stooping on prey. Influxes can occur during severe northern winters. Likely to be confused with Steppe Eagle. – pm/wv

Golden Eagle *Aquila chrysaetos*

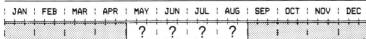

Status and distribution in the region generally unclear. Reports of chicks found in Al Ain area, though no confirming details known and no nests found. Reported September to April in very small numbers, even well away from the mountains. Scarce breeding resident in southern Oman. - rb?

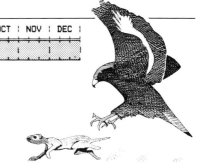

80

Booted Eagle *Hieraaetus pennatus*

JAN	FEB	MAR	APR	MAY	JUN	JUL	AUG	SEP	OCT	NOV	DEC

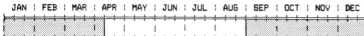

An uncommon passage migrant and winter visitor. Recorded from September to early April in a variety of habitats, including coasts and mountains, and has been reported on the islands. Winters mainly in East and Central Africa. – pm/wv

Bonelli's Eagle *Hieraaetus fasciatus*

JAN	FEB	MAR	APR	MAY	JUN	JUL	AUG	SEP	OCT	NOV	DEC

Scarce and localised mountain resident. Nesting reported from February, and pairs may remain near the nest site all year. Recorded away from the mountains from November to March, mostly immatures, possibly including strays from Iran.

Hunts ground prey, such as hares and partridges, or takes other birds on the wing. Its scarcity worldwide is giving cause for concern, despite its protected status in most of Europe. – rb

Lesser Kestrel *Falco naumanni*

JAN	FEB	MAR	APR	MAY	JUN	JUL	AUG	SEP	OCT	NOV	DEC

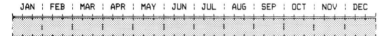

Uncommon passage migrant. Most occur March to April, occasionally August to mid November. Also reported in winter, though sightings are often misidentified *F. tinnunculus*. Favours open country with scattered trees, and although generally scarce, it can occur in small parties. Breeds from southern Spain to Greece, and across Turkey to southern Russia (from where many of the Gulf's migrants probably originate.) Most reach east and southern Africa. – pm

Plate 1

1 — M. West

2 — Author

3 — Author

4 — Author

5 — D. Robinson

1. Young Socotra Cormorant *Phalacrocorax nigrogularis* on breakwater near Dubai.   Text Page 62
2. Socotra Cormorants nesting, Umm al Quwain, early December 1987.   " Page 62
3. Red-billed Tropicbird *Phaethon aethereus,* Qarnayn Island breeding colony, late April 1989.   " Page 61
4. Immature Night Heron *Nycticorax nycticorax,* Zabeel water treatment plant, Dubai, winter 1988.   " Page 64
5. Juvenile Little Grebe *Tachybaptus ruficollis,* Zabeel water treatment plant, November 1989.   " Page 59

Plate 2

6   *M. West*

7   *M. West*

8   *M. West*

9   *D. Robinson*

10   *M. West*

6. White Stork *Ciconia ciconia*, Saffa Park, Dubai, autumn 1984.   Text Page 67
7. Glossy Ibis *Plegadis falcinellus*, Saffa Park, November 1983.   "   Page 67
8. Immature Purple Heron *Ardea purpurea* in Saffa Park.   "   Page 67
9. Dark-phase Western Reef Heron *Egretta gularis*, Abu Dhabi, March 1990.   "   Page 65
10. Juvenile Little Green Heron *Butorides striatus*, near Dubai.   "   Page 64

Plate 3

11   *Author*

12   *M. West*

13   *Author*

14   *M. West*

15   *M. West*

11.   Grey Francolin *Francolinus pondicerianus,* Zabeel water treatment plant, May 1989.   Text Page 84
12.   Eastern race Greylag Goose *Anser anser*, Saffa Park, spring 1982.   "   Page 69
13.   View of Khor Dubai with Greater Flamingoes *Phoenicopterus ruber*, September 1989.   "   Page 68
14.   Black-shouldered Kite *Elanus caeruleus*, Jumeirah, Dubai, 24th February 1984.   "   Page 74
15.   Ferruginous Duck *Aythya nyroca*, Saffa Park pond, autumn 1982.   "   Page 73

Plate 4

16. Black-winged Stilt *Himantopus himantopus*, Ramtha tip, Sharjah, late May 1989.   Text Page 88
17. Cream-coloured Courser *Cursorius cursor*, Saffa Park, July 1989.   "   Page 90
18. Ringed Plover *Charadrius hiaticula*, Ramtha tip, winter 1989.   "   Page 91
19. Stone Curlew *Burhinus oedicnemus*, near Dubai, March 1987.   "   Page 89
20. Kentish Plover *Charadrius alexandrinus* on eggs, Khor Dubai.   "   Page 92

Plate 5

21 Author

24 Author

22 M. West

23 M. West

25 D. Robinson

21. Red-wattled Lapwing *Hoplopterus indicus*, Kalba, East Coast, spring 1989.   Text Page 94
22. Greater Sand Plover *Charadrius leschenaultii*, Khor Dubai.   "   Page 92
23. Pacific Golden Plovers *Pluvialis fulva*, Saffa Park, late April 1982.   "   Page 93
24. White-tailed Plover *Chettusia leucura*, Zabeel water treatment plant, November 1987   "   Page 94
25. Little Stint *Calidris minuta*, wintering at Zabeel water treatment plant, November 1989.   "   Page 95

Plate 6

28   *D. Robinson*

29   *M. West*

26   *D. Robinson*

27   *D. Robinson*

30   *Author*

Plate 7

31   *Author*

32   *M. West*

33   *Author*

34   *D. Robinson*

35   *Author*

31. Common Sandpiper *Actitis hypoleucos*, Zabeel water treatment plant, November 1989.   Text Page 102
32. Winter-plumaged Turnstone *Arenaria interpres*, near Dubai.   "   Page 103
33. Red-necked Phalarope *Phalaropus lobatus*, Emirates Golf Course, autumn 1987.   "   Page 103
34. Immature Black-headed Gull *Larus ridibundus*, Dubai, November 1989.   "   Page 105
35. Sooty Gull *Larus hemprichii*, Qarnayn Island, late April 1989.   "   Page 104

Plate 8

36   *Author*

37   *Author*

38   *Author*

39   *Author*

40   *Author*

36.   First-summer Sandwich Tern *Sterna sandvicensis,* Zabeel water treatment plant, late May 1989.   Text Page 107
37.   Collared Dove *Streptopelia decaocto*, Zabeel water treatment plant.   "   Page 114
38.   Swift Terns *Sterna bergii* and a Lesser Crested Tern *Sterna bengalensis* (2nd left), Umm al Quwain, early July 1989.   "   Page 108/9
39.   Immature White-cheeked Terns *Sterna repressa*, near Khor Fakkan, East Coast, September 1989.   "   Page 111
40.   Saunders' Little Tern *Sterna saundersi*, near Khor Fakkan, September 1989.   "   Page 109

Osprey *Pandion haliaetus*

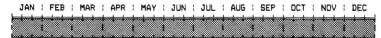

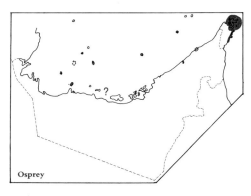
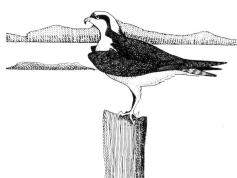

Fairly common and widespread breeding resident, with migrants augmenting the local population in winter months. Seldom found far from water, and often seen perching on posts near tidal mudflats, or resting on harbour breakwaters. Some are found far offshore, where they may use oil well-heads and platforms as their base. The stick nest is built (or re-occupied) on isolated rocky islands and coastlines from October, and 2-3 eggs are laid from November. – RB/WV

Kestrel *Falco tinnunculus*

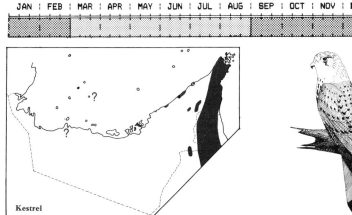

Regular passage migrant and winter visitor. Small numbers resident, nesting from March in large trees, high buildings and more frequently on inaccessible cliffs and ledges in the mountains. Chicks reported late May. Common in autumn and winter, when it is widespread from September to February with passage noted to early April. Females and juveniles more often reported. Found in urban areas, large gardens, rocky outcrops, farms and semi-desert. – WV/PM/rb

Merlin *Falco columbarius*

Vagrant. One adult female recorded in wooded area near Abu Dhabi camel race track on 3rd August 1989. Other reports currently under review. Recorded in Oman in April, and is considered a likely stray throughout the Gulf region. – V

Hobby *Falco subbuteo*

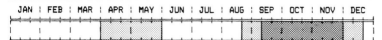

JAN	FEB	MAR	APR	MAY	JUN	JUL	AUG	SEP	OCT	NOV	DEC

Scarce passage migrant from a widespread palaearctic breeding range. Most winter in southern Africa. In spring it occurs in April and May – sometimes from March. More regular from September to late November, with occasional strays in August and December. Favours scrub and semi-desert in open country with scattered trees. – pm

Sooty Falcon *Falco concolor*

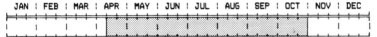

JAN	FEB	MAR	APR	MAY	JUN	JUL	AUG	SEP	OCT	NOV	DEC

Sooty Falcon

Very localised summer breeding visitor to some rocky Arabian Gulf islands (and to seacliffs on tip of Musandam peninsula) from April to October, though typical local nesting details not known. A few specific reports from the mainland, including East Coast. Winters in Madagascar and East Africa. – mb

Note: Annual coloniser of the Hawar Island group (Bahrain) where eggs are laid mid to late summer.

Saker Falcon *Falco cherrug*

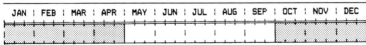

JAN	FEB	MAR	APR	MAY	JUN	JUL	AUG	SEP	OCT	NOV	DEC

A scarce winter visitor from October to April. Many trapped for their use in falconry, and most records are of escaped birds, still wearing leg jesses. A strong fast falcon and an aggressive hunter, pursues Houbara Bustard, hare and even larger mammals. Found in semi-desert, gravel plains and open country with scattered trees. Breeds from eastern Europe across southern Russia to the Far East, with many resident in northern and western Iran. – E/wv

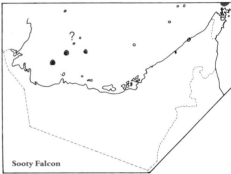

Saker Falcon

Lanner Falcon *Falco biarmicus*

Status uncertain, confused by reports of regular escapes and freed falconers' birds. Generally sedentary within known breeding range, including a small population in Saudi Arabia, though immatures may wander from August to April. However wild birds are undoubtedly scarce. – E/?

Peregrine Falcon *Falco peregrinus*

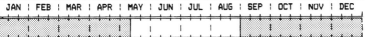

Peregrine Falcon

Winter visitor from northern Europe and Russia where the populations are strongly migratory. Widespread though uncommon from September to March, occasionally to May. A very fast and strong hunter, seen stooping over flocks of waders or perched upright on an exposed branch or rock, often in coastal locations. Freed or escaped falconry birds are regularly seen. Formerly heavily persecuted in Europe and a victim of pesticides, their numbers have recently increased dramatically despite pressures on populations for use in falconry. – E/wv

Barbary Falcon *Falco pelegrinoides*

Status uncertain. Occasional records, usually of escaped or freed birds, still trailing leg jesses. Small numbers kept to train novice falconers in handling. Sightings rare and often misidentified Peregrine Falcon. Older birds are believed to be sedentary within their breeding areas. Reports of small numbers resident in mountains, including Musandam, awaiting verification. – E/rb?

Chukar *Alectoris chukar*

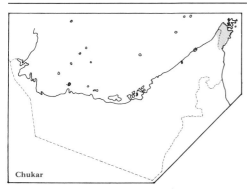

Chukar

Almost all reports in the Emirates are of escaped, or introduced birds. A small population, introduced some years ago, exists in Musandam (Oman) and strays have been reported in the Dibba area. Records from Dubai, Abu Dhabi and other areas are assumed to be released captives. – E/rb?

Sand Partridge *Ammoperdix heyi*

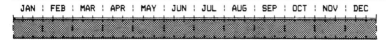

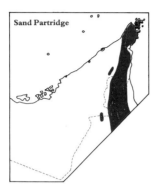

Sand Partridge

Resident in the mountains and foothills. Frequents bare rocky slopes, wadis and mountain sides and is rarely found away from this habitat. Although shy, its whirring flight usually betrays its presence, revealing sometimes up to 20 in a covey. 4–6 eggs are laid in a stony scrape from March to May. – RB

Note: Should not be confused with Grey Francolin, which occurs in some mountain cultivations.

Grey Francolin *Francolinus pondicerianus* Plate 3

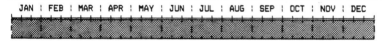

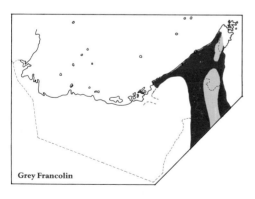

Grey Francolin

Common, even abundant resident in some areas. Many populations introduced. Has successfully colonised cultivations, less arid scrub and wooded areas, and is seldom found far from water. Loud raucous repetetive call is diagnostic, and usually first indication of their presence. Roosts in trees. Breeds from January, laying 4–9 eggs in a lined scrape on the ground. Chicks are common from mid May. – RB

Note: Sometimes confused with Sand Partridge in suburbs of Gulf coastal towns, where only Grey Francolin is likely to occur.

Quail *Coturnix coturnix*

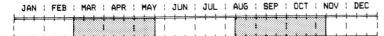

| JAN | FEB | MAR | APR | MAY | JUN | JUL | AUG | SEP | OCT | NOV | DEC |

Scarce passage migrant, individuals reported March to May, and August to November. Most occur March, and mid September to early November. Often discovered accidentally when flushed from its hiding place under a bush, rock or grass tussock. Captive populations are bred commercially, and escapes likely. – pm/E

Water Rail *Rallus aquaticus*

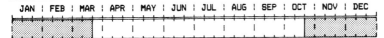

| JAN | FEB | MAR | APR | MAY | JUN | JUL | AUG | SEP | OCT | NOV | DEC |

Scarce and irregular winter visitor from late October to mid March, exceptionally from August to May. Found in marshes or beside ponds with thick border vegetation, where it skulks and may be overlooked. – wv

Note: An opportunist breeder, nesting in small numbers in eastern Saudi Arabia and rated a potential breeding species in the UAE.

Spotted Crake *Porzana porzana*

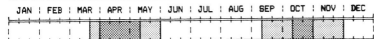

| JAN | FEB | MAR | APR | MAY | JUN | JUL | AUG | SEP | OCT | NOV | DEC |

Regular passage migrant, late March to early May (later some years), and September to November. Prefers damp grassy patches and swamps with adjacent border cover, often two or three birds at one location. May remain for some weeks at a favoured site before resuming migration. Breeds widely across the European and Soviet temperate zone as well as Iran and the Far East. – PM

Baillon's Crake *Porzana pusilla*

JAN	FEB	MAR	APR	MAY	JUN	JUL	AUG	SEP	OCT	NOV	DEC

Uncommon and irregular passage migrant, most recorded late March to April. Migration patterns unclear, individuals also reported February and June to November (mostly in the Dubai area). Favours thick damp vegetation, and as other crakes, is very shy and skulking. Most likely to be found in ditches, at sewage outflows and water treatment plants with plenty of undergrowth. Winters in Pakistan, India, Africa and Arabia. Some sightings may be confused with Little Crake. *P. parva,* see page 168.– pm.

Corncrake *Crex crex*

JAN	FEB	MAR	APR	MAY	JUN	JUL	AUG	SEP	OCT	NOV	DEC

Scarce passage migrant late September to October. Less than a handful of sightings mid March to mid April. Very difficult to observe. Skulks in patches of long grass or thick low bushes in parks, cultivations and large gardens. – pm

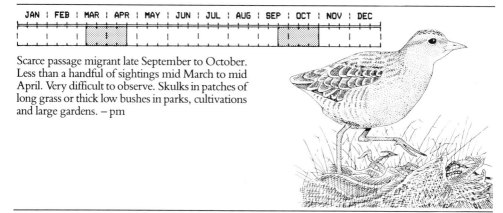

Moorhen *Gallinula chloropus*

JAN	FEB	MAR	APR	MAY	JUN	JUL	AUG	SEP	OCT	NOV	DEC

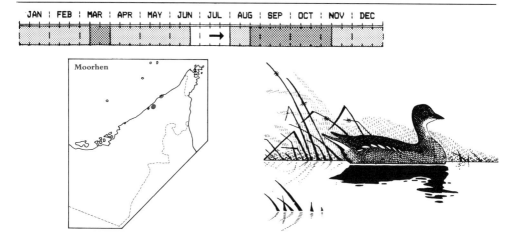

Moorhen

Fairly common passage migrant, occasional winter visitor and casual breeder. Most recorded August to December, occasionally to March, when further passage and nest prospecting can occur. Prefers overgrown freshwater margins and is usually shy.

First two breeding records for UAE in 1989 when single chicks seen at Kalba (mid April) and Sharjah (mid May). – PM/wv/cb

Also breeds in Oman, Bahrain, eastern Saudi Arabia and Qatar from March to June.

Purple Gallinule *Porphyrio porphyrio*

Rare vagrant to the Southern Gulf region. One occurred in the grounds of the Jebel Ali Hotel in late October 1984, one of only a handful of records in Arabia. – V

Coot *Fulica atra*

JAN	FEB	MAR	APR	MAY	JUN	JUL	AUG	SEP	OCT	NOV	DEC

Common winter visitor to mountain reservoirs, water treatment plants and other large freshwater ponds with nearby grazing. Occasionally on sheltered coastal harbours on passage. Main arrival late October, with peak December to February, before departing end of March, with stragglers to early May some years. Occurs in largest numbers during severe northern winters when lakes and rivers are ice-bound. – WV

Common Crane *Grus grus*

Winter vagrant. One at Khor Kalba mid September 1977. Possibly more common on East Coast in autumn than records suggest. One on Qarnayn Island in early October 1984. Other reports, for which no details are available, include six together at Abu Dhabi. – V

Demoiselle Crane *Anthropoides virgo*

Winter vagrant. Reports include one at Abu Dhabi from early October to mid November 1983, and one there late December 1983, probably same bird. Also reported from Al Ain, dates unknown. More common in Oman. – V

Houbara Bustard *Chlamydotis undulata*

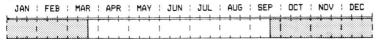

JAN	FEB	MAR	APR	MAY	JUN	JUL	AUG	SEP	OCT	NOV	DEC

Former breeding species, but now a critically scarce winter visitor, many birds hunted shortly after their arrival. Present from September to March, and most likely to be found between November and February. A bird of desert scrub, undulating dunes and stony gravel plains with sparse vegetation. Captive breeding programmes are underway in the UAE to prevent its steady decline, with the aim of reintroducing numbers into the wild. – wv

Houbara

Oystercatcher *Haematopus ostralegus*

JAN	FEB	MAR	APR	MAY	JUN	JUL	AUG	SEP	OCT	NOV	DEC

A regular passage migrant and winter visitor, with small numbers present throughout the summer. Widespread on coasts, creeks and lagoons, though rarely numerous. Up to 100 birds may occupy a favoured site August to March. Occasionally on exposed beaches on passage. The brown-mantled eastern race *H. o. longipes*, from Asia Minor, central USSR and western Siberia commonest sub-species occurring. – WV/pm/sv

Black-winged Stilt *Himantopus himantopus*   Plate 4

JAN	FEB	MAR	APR	MAY	JUN	JUL	AUG	SEP	OCT	NOV	DEC

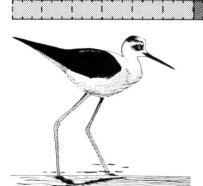

Black-winged Stilt

A common passage migrant, winter visitor and casual summer breeding species. Regular and often widespread in small flocks late summer and autumn on shallow ponds, mudflats, water treatment plants and sewage dumps. Less common from late winter to June, except at breeding sites where it nests from late March if suitable conditions available. Breeding sites include Ramtha tip (Sharjah) and Kalba, the latter providing the UAE's first breeding record in spring 1988. It has also nested in east Saudi Arabia, Qatar and Oman in recent years. – PM/wv/cb

Avocet *Recurvirostra avosetta*

JAN	FEB	MAR	APR	MAY	JUN	JUL	AUG	SEP	OCT	NOV	DEC

A scarce and erratic passage migrant and winter visitor from late August to April, with numbers increasing slightly from November to March. Found in small parties on shallow tidal mudflats and freshwater marshes, and is often very wary. Likely to be found at Khor Dubai during most of the period. – pm/wv

Avocets
with Black-winged Stilt

Crab Plover *Dromas ardeola*

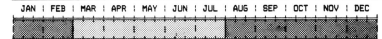

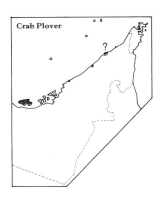

A localised passage migrant and winter visitor, usually found in loose flocks in sheltered lagoons on the Arabian Gulf coast. Greatest numbers occur at Khor al Beidah, where it is recorded in all months, numbering over 200 from August to February. On passage it may turn up on creeks and shorelines. Its breeding status is not clear in the UAE; nesting has been reported at Abu al Abyadh, west of Abu Dhabi, and is suspected at Khor al Beidah. This species generally requires further study. – WV/pm/rb?

Stone Curlew *Burhinus oedicnemus*   Plate 4

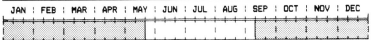

Scarce passage migrant and winter visitor mid September to May. Favours areas of gravel plains and semi-desert, its cryptic plumage providing camouflage from predators. A unique species in the wader family, as it rarely depends on water. Regularly hunted by falconers. Breeds across Europe to India including parts of the Middle East, and is bred in captivity in the UAE. – pm/wv/E

Cream-coloured Courser *Cursorius cursor* — Plate 4

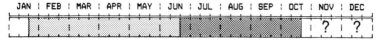

JAN	FEB	MAR	APR	MAY	JUN	JUL	AUG	SEP	OCT	NOV	DEC
										?	?

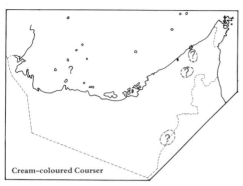

Cream-coloured Courser

Resident and dispersive. Breeds on flat gravel areas, surrounded by sandy desert and often away from water. Exact nesting areas still undiscovered, though indications are that locations vary annually. More likely to be seen from late June to mid-October, when small parties (occasionally large flocks) congregate in less arid areas prior to dispersal, usually near the Gulf coast. Generally irregularly recorded, and migrants may also occur. Probably nests from March to May. – rb/pm?

Collared Pratincole *Glareola pratincola*

JAN	FEB	MAR	APR	MAY	JUN	JUL	AUG	SEP	OCT	NOV	DEC
				→							

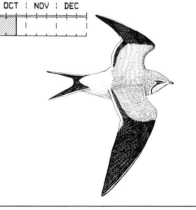

Regular spring and autumn passage migrant, found in small numbers on coasts, inland shallow pools and flooded grassland. Main passage is late August to September with variable late spring passage in April and May. Less frequently at other times. Care not to mistake it for the similar, though rarely recorded Black-winged Pratincole. Considered a casual nesting species in Arabia. – PM

Black-winged Pratincole *Glareola nordmanni*

Vagrant. One near Khor Dubai on 10th December 1984, only accepted record to date. A long distance migrant between the Russian steppes and southern Africa and generally overflies Gulf on passage. Most reports are of mistakenly identified *G. pratincola*. – V

Little Pratincole *Glareola lactea*

A winter vagrant from the Indian sub-continent and the Far East, with less than five records since 1978, all from November to early March. Favours damp areas, creeks, pools, marshes and mudflats. – V

Little Ringed Plover *Charadrius dubius*

| JAN | FEB | MAR | APR | MAY | JUN | JUL | AUG | SEP | OCT | NOV | DEC |

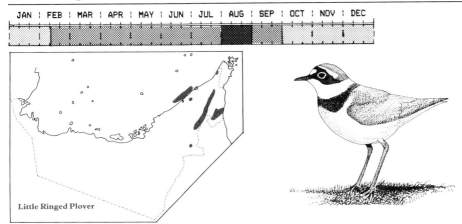

Little Ringed Plover

Common passage migrant and breeding summer visitor to inland puddles of fresh and brackish water, sewage treatment plants and some creek shores. Most common from February to September, with peak passage in August. Few October to January. Quick to take advantage of new breeding sites, where it nests from April to late June, laying 2 or 3 eggs. Might be found at pools in remote desert or even in the mountains, but should not be confused with larger Ringed Plover, which rarely occurs inland. – PM/MB

Ringed Plover *Charadrius hiaticula* — Plate 4

| JAN | FEB | MAR | APR | MAY | JUN | JUL | AUG | SEP | OCT | NOV | DEC |

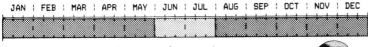

Common passage migrant and sometimes abundant winter visitor to coastal creeks and tidal mudflats. Main passage occurs from mid August, with an autumn peak at the end of October when several hundred may be present at favoured sites. Few in June and July. Occurs in small numbers at inland marshes and open water during peak migration. The darker Siberian race, *C. h. tundrae* has been recorded at Khor Dubai, and may be prevalent throughout. – PM/WV/sv

Caspian Plover *Charadrius asiaticus*

| JAN | FEB | MAR | APR | MAY | JUN | JUL | AUG | SEP | OCT | NOV | DEC |

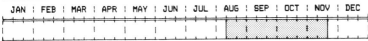

Rare autumn passage migrant, tolerant of drier habitat, found on coastal dunes and grassland, and at fresh and brackish standing water. Occurs mid August to September, less frequently to November. – pm

Lesser Sand Plover *Charadrius mongolus*

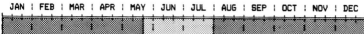

| JAN | FEB | MAR | APR | MAY | JUN | JUL | AUG | SEP | OCT | NOV | DEC |

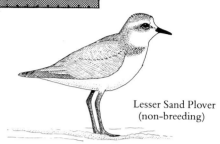

Common passage migrant and winter visitor to coasts, tidal pools and creek mudflats in variable numbers (over 1,000 at some sites), with some remaining over the summer. Main southbound passage from August, peaking in October, when some also occur away from the coast. Northbound passage most evident in April. Usually in larger numbers than Greater Sand Plover in mixed flocks. – PM/WV/sv

Lesser Sand Plover
(non-breeding)

Greater Sand Plover *Charadrius leschenaultii*   Plate 5

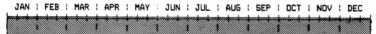

| JAN | FEB | MAR | APR | MAY | JUN | JUL | AUG | SEP | OCT | NOV | DEC |

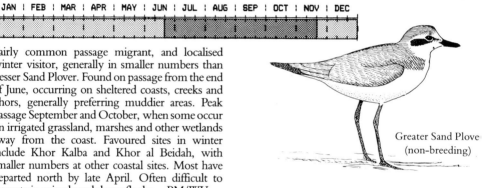

Fairly common passage migrant, and localised winter visitor, generally in smaller numbers than Lesser Sand Plover. Found on passage from the end of June, occurring on sheltered coasts, creeks and khors, generally preferring muddier areas. Peak passage September and October, when some occur on irrigated grassland, marshes and other wetlands away from the coast. Favoured sites in winter include Khor Kalba and Khor al Beidah, with smaller numbers at other coastal sites. Most have departed north by late April. Often difficult to separate in mixed sandplover flocks. – PM/WV

Greater Sand Plover
(non-breeding)

Kentish Plover *Charadrius alexandrinus*   Plate 4

| JAN | FEB | MAR | APR | MAY | JUN | JUL | AUG | SEP | OCT | NOV | DEC |

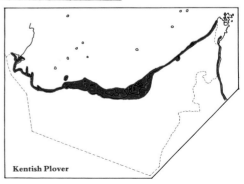

Kentish Plover

Common breeding resident, and in winter numbers are supplemented by birds from the Balkans, Turkey and south-east Russia. Found on most shallow tidal mudflats and creeks, and occasionally at inland patches of brackish water, particularly in autumn. Lays up to four eggs from March onwards, often on exposed banks or just above the high tide line. – RB/WV/PM

Dotterel *Charadrius morinellus*

Vagrant. Less than ten records, mostly Gulf coast and usually in open grassy areas. Sighted in every month from July to December. Up to six have occurred together (Dubai, mid December 1970) but most reports are of single or pairs of birds in non-breeding plumage. – V

Pacific Golden Plover *Pluvialis fulva*   Plate 5

JAN	FEB	MAR	APR	MAY	JUN	JUL	AUG	SEP	OCT	NOV	DEC

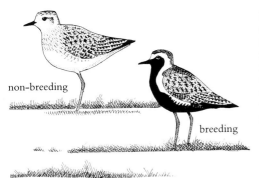

non-breeding

breeding

Fairly common, though localised winter visitor and passage migrant. Occurs in loose approachable flocks on open grassland and at some coastal mudflats. A long-stay winter visitor and one of the farthest travelled of shorebirds wintering in the Gulf. It nests in the Arctic tundra of NE Siberia and arrives in the UAE in late August, some staying until mid May (though few after March). Breeding plumage notable in August and from April. Sometimes confused with Golden Plover (see page 168.). – WV/PM

Grey Plover *Pluvialis squatarola*

JAN	FEB	MAR	APR	MAY	JUN	JUL	AUG	SEP	OCT	NOV	DEC

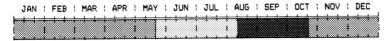

A long-distance passage migrant and winter visitor, commonly found in flocks of several hundred, or scattered loosely at favoured sites on coastal mudflats and freshwater margins. Main southward passage is from mid August to mid October, whilst less obvious northward peak is April, many migrating between nesting areas in central Siberia and wintering grounds in southern Africa. Good numbers winter, and a handful of non-breeding birds can be present throughout the summer. – WV/PM/sv

Grey Plover
(winter)

Red-wattled Lapwing *Hoplopterus indicus*   Plate 5

| JAN | FEB | MAR | APR | MAY | JUN | JUL | AUG | SEP | OCT | NOV | DEC |

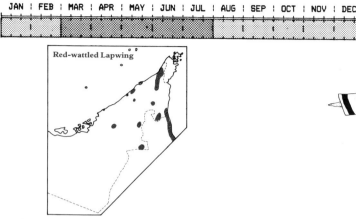

Resident and dispersive, most appearing only during the breeding season, when it nests adjacent to newly formed and temporary stretches of water, including mountain reservoirs, water-filled pits, sewage dumps, pools and wet wadis. Common from March, when breeding activity starts, and young are present from May. Generally vacates nest sites by September, and is scarce until late February. Passage may occur March and November. Some winter in Ras al Khaimah cultivated areas. - rb/pm/ mb?

Sociable Plover *Chettusia gregaria*

Rare vagrant from a relatively small breeding area in Central Soviet Asia. Winters in NE Africa, Iraq and NW India. Solitary birds recorded on irrigated grassland in Saffa Park in November 1984 and February 1986. – V

White-tailed Plover *Chettusia leucura*   Plate 5

| JAN | FEB | MAR | APR | MAY | JUN | JUL | AUG | SEP | OCT | NOV | DEC |

Rather uncommon central Asian migrant, most likely to occur October to December, though recorded irregularly all months late August to April (and twice in May). Favours shallow tidal mudflats and inland freshwater margins, occurring at water treatment plants, sewage works and open irrigated grassland away from the coast. Usually found singly, though has occurred in small groups. – pm/ wv

Lapwing *Vanellus vanellus*

| JAN | FEB | MAR | APR | MAY | JUN | JUL | AUG | SEP | OCT | NOV | DEC |

Scarce and sporadic winter visitor to creek edges, mudflats, grassland and freshwater margins, although it may tolerate drier habitats. Fairly regular October to December, occasionally to January, and sometimes occurs in small groups. – wv

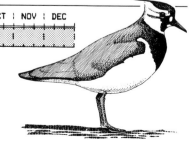

Great Knot *Calidris tenuirostris*

Vagrant. One at Khor Kalba for several days in November 1986, and five at Khor al Beidah, Umm al Quwain 7-9th March 1990. Usual wintering grounds include Australasia. – V

Note: Appears to be scarce autumn and winter visitor to Batinah coast of northern Oman from late August. Lack of observers on the Emirates' East Coast may be reason for lack of records of this and other rare Siberian waders.

Knot *Calidris canutus*

Vagrant. One in breeding plummage on 16th June 1978 on Das Island. Reported less than a handful of other times through sightings lack substantiating detail. Generally rare throughout Arabia. Few records in Oman in April, May, August and October. – V

Sanderling *Calidris alba*

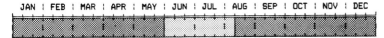

| JAN | FEB | MAR | APR | MAY | JUN | JUL | AUG | SEP | OCT | NOV | DEC |

Passage migrant and winter visitor from August to May to sandy coasts and shorelines, where it is an active feeder, though seldom in large numbers. Also occurs on inland shallow muddy creeks and pools during peak spring passage in April and May. Breeds in the extreme northern tundra, and winters around the coastlines of all the world's southern continents. Few remain in summer. – PM/WV/sv

Little Stint *Calidris minuta*   Plate 5

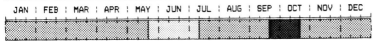

| JAN | FEB | MAR | APR | MAY | JUN | JUL | AUG | SEP | OCT | NOV | DEC |

Very common long-distance migrant, many pausing to feed in the Southern Gulf before continuing on to Africa. Flocks of several hundred (sometimes thousands) are found on mudflats and tidal creeks in autumn. Numbers increase quickly from August, and southerly passage peaks in early October. Some overwinter, and numbers drop steadily March to mid May. Non-breeders present in summer. – PM/WV/sv

Temminck's Stint *Calidris temminckii*

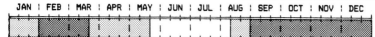

| JAN | FEB | MAR | APR | MAY | JUN | JUL | AUG | SEP | OCT | NOV | DEC |

Fairly common passage migrant, fewer in winter. Occurs singly (or in loose groups) at freshwater margins, marshes and mudflats, favouring water treatment plants and associated settlement beds. Main southerly passage from the end of August, with numbers dropping by late December. Less common in spring, when small numbers can occur until May (though few after March). – PM/wv

Curlew Sandpiper *Calidris ferruginea*

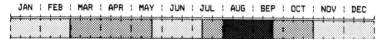

| JAN | FEB | MAR | APR | MAY | JUN | JUL | AUG | SEP | OCT | NOV | DEC |

Very common passage migrant, some overwintering. Migrants start arriving in mid July, en route to Southern Africa. The species' relatively small breeding area on the Taimyr peninsula in Siberia produces prolific passage in the Gulf, where flocks of many thousand birds may occur on mudflats and creeks from Arabia to the Far East. Most passage is over by late October and few remain for the winter. Spring passage is from March to May after which only a few are present in summer. Often difficult to distinguish in non-breeding plumage from Dunlin in large roosts. – PM/wv/sv

Dunlin *Calidris alpina*   Plate 6

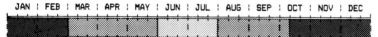

| JAN | FEB | MAR | APR | MAY | JUN | JUL | AUG | SEP | OCT | NOV | DEC |

Abundant passage migrant and winter visitor, with main passage from early September, when breeding plumage may still be visible during moult. Dramatic passage activity in October, followed by winter consolidation on mudflats and creeks towards the winter months. A regular visitor to Khor Dubai in thousands from October to February. Rarely favours inland areas, except during peak passage, when it might occur at sewage works, brackish pools and pond edges. Small numbers, mostly non-breeders remain during the summer. Biometrics of plumage features indicate that a number of sub-species may occur, including Siberian race *C. a. sakhalina* in autumn, with a marked increase of *C. a. alpina* as winter approaches. – WV/PM/sv

Dunlin (winter)

Broad-billed Sandpiper *Limicola falcinellus*

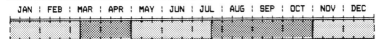

JAN	FEB	MAR	APR	MAY	JUN	JUL	AUG	SEP	OCT	NOV	DEC

Common but localised on passage, some overwintering. Influx commences late July, with numbers increasing to a peak in October. Smaller numbers occur at other times, including a less obvious passage in spring. Feeds at coastal mudflats, tidal pools and other shallow fresh and brackish water margins (sometimes amongst sandplover flocks). Studies have shown that a large proportion of the known Scandinavian population migrates through the region (4,000 were counted at Khor Dubai during passage in mid October 1986). – PM/WV

Ruff *Philomachus pugnax*

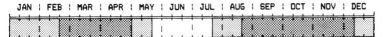

JAN	FEB	MAR	APR	MAY	JUN	JUL	AUG	SEP	OCT	NOV	DEC

Common passage migrant and winter visitor, from late July to early December and from late February to April. Less common December to February and May. Favoured habitats include creeks, mudflats, pond edges, damp meadows and sewage treatment plants. There is considerable size variation between the sexes, the male Ruff being almost a third larger than the female Reeve. – PM/wv

Ruff (winter)

Jack Snipe *Lymnocryptes minimus*

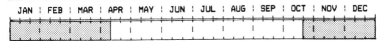

JAN	FEB	MAR	APR	MAY	JUN	JUL	AUG	SEP	OCT	NOV	DEC

A scarce and skulking winter visitor usually flushed by accident. Occurs late October to early April in a similar habitat to Common Snipe, including sewage ditches, damp overgrown grassland and pond edges. Probably under-recorded. – wv

Common Snipe *Gallinago gallinago*

Plate 6

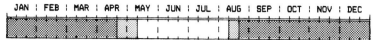

JAN	FEB	MAR	APR	MAY	JUN	JUL	AUG	SEP	OCT	NOV	DEC

Regular passage migrant and winter visitor, often flushed by chance, when its rasping call is heard. First arrivals appear in mid August with a peak October to December. Favours marshes, pond edges, flooded grassland, water treatment plants with rank vegetation and damp ditches. Usually occurs singly, but several may occur together during peak passage. Most have returned north by mid April. – PM/WV

Great Snipe *Gallinago media*

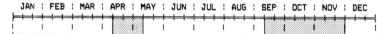

JAN	FEB	MAR	APR	MAY	JUN	JUL	AUG	SEP	OCT	NOV	DEC

Very scarce passage migrant recorded mid September to November, and less than a handful of times in April and May. Winter reports likely confused with *G. gallinago*. Conversely may also be overlooked on passage due to similarity to Common Snipe. Prefers marshy areas but can tolerate drier ground. – pm

Pintail Snipe *Gallinago stenura*

Rare winter visitor. One was recorded at Abu Dhabi from early December 1977 to early January 1978 and another in early March 1979. Breeds in northern and eastern Russia, adjacent to rivers, marshes and pools but may favour less damp areas than other snipes, a habitat widespread in its sub-tropical wintering grounds on the Sub-continent. Possibly overlooked due to its similarities to Common Snipe. – V

Woodcock *Scolopax rusticola*

Vagrant from central Asian wintering grounds. A handful of autumn and winter records, mostly in ones and twos November to January near Arabian Gulf coast. Generally favours damp ground cover beneath trees or in thick scrub near water. – V

Black-tailed Godwit *Limosa limosa* — Plate 6

JAN	FEB	MAR	APR	MAY	JUN	JUL	AUG	SEP	OCT	NOV	DEC

Regular passage migrant and winter visitor from August to March (most September to November), few April to July. Occurs in small numbers on mudflats and creeks, usually maintaining separate flock from more common Bar-tailed Godwit. Also likely at freshwater margins and grassland. Most are of the nominate race, from breeding areas in Europe and western Asia. – PM/WV

Bar-tailed Godwit *Limosa lapponica*

JAN	FEB	MAR	APR	MAY	JUN	JUL	AUG	SEP	OCT	NOV	DEC

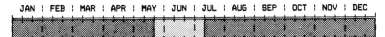

Very common passage migrant and winter visitor to coastal mudflats and shallow creeks. First returning migrants seen mid July, from breeding grounds in northern Scandinavia and the Taimyr peninsula in the high Arctic. Rarely at freshwater (unlike the Black-tailed Godwit), and is wary in flocks, which often exceed one thousand at Khor Dubai late August to April. – WV/PM/sv

Whimbrel *Numenius phaeopus* — Plate 6

JAN	FEB	MAR	APR	MAY	JUN	JUL	AUG	SEP	OCT	NOV	DEC

Fairly regular passage migrant and localised winter visitor, commonest in autumn from late August to November at freshwater pools, sewage outflows, tidal edges and damp meadows. Winters on coastlines and khors, though scarce in Dubai after October. A light northbound passage occurs in April. Less wary than Curlew. – PM/wv

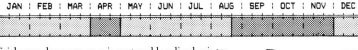

Curlew *Numenius arquata*

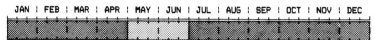

| JAN | FEB | MAR | APR | MAY | JUN | JUL | AUG | SEP | OCT | NOV | DEC |

Common migrant and winter visitor, with steady increase in numbers on favoured coasts and mudflats from early July until November. Less common in spring, and most depart by April. Small numbers remain in the summer. Often occurs in open parkland on passage. Winters on coasts from the Far East around most of the Sub-continent, Arabia, Africa and Europe. *N. a. orientalis* occurs, its larger size and longer bill sometimes suggesting Far-eastern Curlew *N. madagascariensis* (see page 169). – WV/PM/sv

Spotted Redshank *Tringa erythropus*

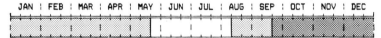

| JAN | FEB | MAR | APR | MAY | JUN | JUL | AUG | SEP | OCT | NOV | DEC |

Irregular passage migrant and winter visitor usually occurring singly at pond margins, flooded grassland and marshes, occasionally on sheltered creeks. Most likely to be seen September to December, occasionally in all months August to May. – pm/wv

Redshank *Tringa totanus*

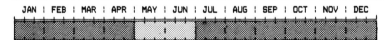

| JAN | FEB | MAR | APR | MAY | JUN | JUL | AUG | SEP | OCT | NOV | DEC |

Very common passage migrant and winter visitor. Large numbers start passing through in mid summer, with several hundred present on favoured mudflats from July until April. Some non-breeding birds oversummer. Many pass through on way to East and Central Africa, from nesting areas which span across northern Europe to north-east China. Also occurs in smaller numbers at inland sites, including sewage plants, ponds, marshes and standing water. – WV/PM/sv

Marsh Sandpiper *Tringa stagnatilis*

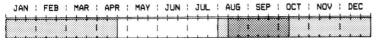

Uncommon migrant, most occur on autumn passage, less frequent in winter. Generally likely August to mid March, occasionally to April, often solitary or in small loose groups. Favours shallow ponds, sewage plants and occasionally sheltered tidal pools and mudflats. – pm/wv

Greenshank *Tringa nebularia*

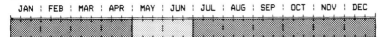

Common passage migrant and winter visitor from July to April, occasionally May and June, from breeding areas in the northern temperate zone. Widespread and quite common on coastal mudflats, pond edges, water treatment plants and sewage outlets. Usually occurs singly, though may form small flocks on passage. Wintering grounds include Indo–China and the whole of Africa south of the Sahara. – WV/PM/sv

Green Sandpiper *Tringa ochropus*

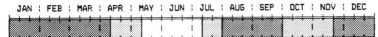

Fairly common passage migrant and winter visitor, mid July to early April. Occasionally other months. Peak southerly passage August and September, scarce October to mid November. Found away from exposed coasts, favouring sheltered creeks and breakwaters, wadi pools, ponds and ditches, often singly, though small parties occur on passage. – PM/WV

Wood Sandpiper *Tringa glareola*

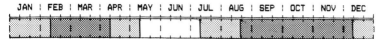

| JAN | FEB | MAR | APR | MAY | JUN | JUL | AUG | SEP | OCT | NOV | DEC |

Passage migrant and winter visitor sharing some habitat with Green Sandpiper, though generally in more open areas, including shallow brackish and freshwater pools, irrigated grassland and sewage treatment plants. Small numbers from mid July, though most active on passage from late August, peaking September to early December. Less obvious spring passage, February to early April, stragglers remaining to May. Has occurred in June. – PM/WV

Terek Sandpiper *Xenus cinereus* Plate 6

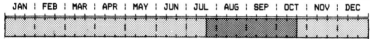

| JAN | FEB | MAR | APR | MAY | JUN | JUL | AUG | SEP | OCT | NOV | DEC |

A fairly common, though localised passage migrant and winter visitor. Feeds at shorelines, tidal pools, mudflats and creek edges, seldom inland. Seen in all months, with numbers peaking from late July to October (several hundred recorded at Khor al Beidah) with a less obvious passage from March to May. Regularly wintering sites include Khor al Beidah, Al Jazeera Khor, Khor Kalba and the lagoons around Abu Dhabi. – PM/WV

Common Sandpiper *Actitis hypoleucos* Plate 7

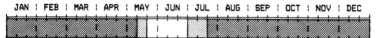

| JAN | FEB | MAR | APR | MAY | JUN | JUL | AUG | SEP | OCT | NOV | DEC |

Very common and widespread passage migrant and winter visitor seen around most inland freshwater ponds, water treatment plants and irrigated grassland late July to early May. A solitary feeder, though several may be present at one site particularly on passage. Rarely on mudflats, though sometimes on shorelines, rocky coasts and creek edges. – PM/WV

Turnstone *Arenaria interpres* Plate 7

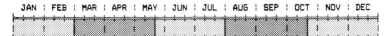

JAN	FEB	MAR	APR	MAY	JUN	JUL	AUG	SEP	OCT	NOV	DEC

Common autumn passage migrant from nesting grounds on the Arctic tundra. Numbers peak August to October, with a less obvious spring passage March to mid May. Occurs at other times in much smaller numbers. First year birds may remain over the summer. Found at shorelines, mudflats and creeks. On autumn passage favours sewage treatment plants and waste tips, sometimes far inland. – PM/wv

Red-necked Phalarope *Phalaropus lobatus* Plate 7

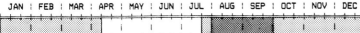

JAN	FEB	MAR	APR	MAY	JUN	JUL	AUG	SEP	OCT	NOV	DEC

A regular and fairly common migrant found on inland pools, ponds, lagoons and creeks, when it can be very tame. Most common in autumn, from late July, peaking in August and September. Some remain in favoured locations until early November. Light spring passage mid February to early April, and some may occasionally oversummer. Large concentrations overwinter on the edge of the continental shelf in the Arabian Sea, although small numbers have been recorded wintering in Arabian Gulf waters. – PM/WV

Grey Phalarope *Phalaropus fulicarius*

Uncommon winter visitor to Arabian Sea offshore feeding areas, where small numbers mix with large flocks of Red-necked Phalarope. Rare at other times. 10 in breeding plumage reported in Arabian Gulf in late May 1989. Possibly more regular in Gulf when abundant upwelled food supply decreases in Arabian Sea late winter and spring. – wv

Arctic Skua *Stercorarius parasiticus*

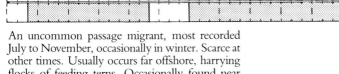

JAN	FEB	MAR	APR	MAY	JUN	JUL	AUG	SEP	OCT	NOV	DEC

An uncommon passage migrant, most recorded July to November, occasionally in winter. Scarce at other times. Usually occurs far offshore, harrying flocks of feeding terns. Occasionally found near coasts, ports and fishing harbours. Generally winters further south than Pomarine Skua. – PM/wv

Pomarine Skua *Stercorarius pomarinus*

| JAN | FEB | MAR | APR | MAY | JUN | JUL | AUG | SEP | OCT | NOV | DEC |

Fairly common passage migrant and regular winter visitor, often far from shore, and sometimes in small parties. Smaller numbers present throughout the year, but more likely March to May, and August to October. Regularly occurs inside the Arabian Gulf straying near harbours and ports, often harrying gulls and terns. – PM/WV

Long-tailed Skua *Stercorarius longicaudus*

Vagrant. Two adults reported offshore Fujeirah 26th March 1989, and another two found off Dubai 5th April 1989, first records for the UAE. Adult strays most likely to occur in spring, when migrating north into Arabia Sea in error. Breeds in Arctic polar regions May to September. Has been recorded on Batinah coast of Oman in May. – V

Great Skua *Stercorarius skua*

Vagrant. One was reported off the coast near Dubai on the 14th February 1989. This stray might be a young bird of either the nominate form from the North Atlantic or one of its southern representatives, especially *lönnbergii,* which breeds in the subantarctic islands south of the Indian Ocean, and which are hard to tell apart. – V.

Note: The southern forms are sometimes considered as specifically distinct, Lönnberg's (Brown) Skua and Southern Great (Antarctic) Skua.

Sooty (Hemprich's) Gull *Larus hemprichii*   Plate 7

| JAN | FEB | MAR | APR | MAY | JUN | JUL | AUG | SEP | OCT | NOV | DEC |

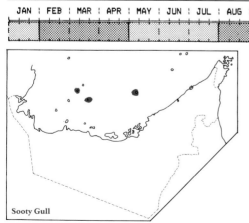

Sooty Gull

Resident in small numbers, and supplemented by breeding visitors in spring. Nests from mid April to August on a handful of Gulf islands in small numbers (estimated at several hundred only), where its chicks are fed on eggs from adjacent tern colonies. Common inshore February to April prior to nesting, and August to October following dispersal. Frequents fishing harbours and ports, and sometimes seen in mixed flocks at fishing catches, particularly on the East Coast. Reported feeding at offshore oil installations. – RB/mb/pm

Great Black-headed Gull *Larus ichthyaetus*

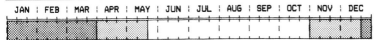

Fairly uncommon. Generally present in small numbers from November (some years from October), with numbers increasing from December. Most are gone by March, few remaining to May. Most likely to be found along coasts, in harbours and sheltered creeks, often fishing with other gulls and terns at fish shoals inshore. Also occurs at sewage works, mudflats, water treatment plants and other inland gull roosts in smaller numbers. Adults start to acquire their black hood in January. – WV/pm

(non-breeding)

Black-headed Gull *Larus ridibundus*

Plate 7

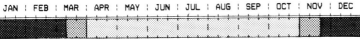

An abundant winter visitor, with a large influx into the region from late November to March, when they are found on all coasts, creeks and harbours. Regular visitor to sewage works, mudflats and water treatment plants, forming large roosts, and occasionally found far inland. Some non-breeding birds oversummer. May be confused in winter plumage with Slender-billed Gull *L. genei*. – WV

Brown-headed Gull *Larus brunnicephalus*

Rarely recorded in Arabia, though possibly overlooked due to its similarity to the Black-headed Gull. Has occurred in the southern Arabian Gulf and the Gulf of Oman late November to February, in the company of other gulls. Regularly winters around the Indian sub-continent. – V or wv?

Slender-billed Gull *Larus genei*

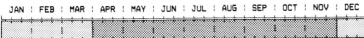

Present throughout the year as a non-breeding visitor. Less common in some areas in winter when it is largely displaced by the Black-headed Gull, with which it is often confused. An active feeder it favours shallow lagoons and creeks, where it occasionally plunge-dives. Large roosts may be present from April to November on mudflats and creeks. – PM/WV/sv

Common Gull *Larus canus*

Winter vagrant to the UAE and generally uncommon throughout Gulf region. Recorded singly, November to February in coastal locations, including harbours, creeks and sewage works. – V

Lesser Black-backed Gull *Larus fuscus*

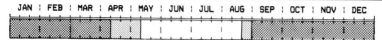

JAN	FEB	MAR	APR	MAY	JUN	JUL	AUG	SEP	OCT	NOV	DEC

(immature)

Common passage migrant and winter visitor to coasts, creeks and inshore islands. Large numbers from September to early April when first-winter birds heavily outnumber older birds. Some immatures present in summer months. – PM/WV

Note: The taxonomy of these large gulls is confusing and still poorly understood. The medium-grey-backed forms *L. (f.) taimyrensis* (large) and *L. (f.) barabensis* (small), sometimes also referred to as *L. (c.) mongolus* appear to be commonest in the Emirates, with smaller numbers of darker-backed *L. f. heuglini* (large, streaked head in winter) and *L. f. fuscus* (small, unstreaked head) occurring mainly on migration and wintering further south. Confusion is likely with *L. cachinnans* and *L. armenicus*, and the immatures of all of them are hard to tell apart.

Yellow-legged Gull *Larus cachinnans*

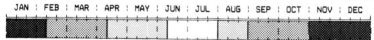

JAN	FEB	MAR	APR	MAY	JUN	JUL	AUG	SEP	OCT	NOV	DEC

Common passage migrant and winter visitor from September (some arrive in August) to early April scavenging along coastlines at fishing harbours, sewage works, lagoons and occasionally further inland. Small numbers remain during the summer. Adults distinguished from confusing Lesser Black-back types by slightly larger size, more white at wingtips, bright yellow legs, pale grey back and prominent red spot near tip of lower portion of bill. Immatures far outnumber adults, and confusion is likely with other large gulls (except Great Black-headed Gull). Breeds in Central Asia. – PM/WV

Note: This species still treated by some as sub-species of Herring Gull *L.argentatus*. Taxonomy of these large gulls is still not agreed, though from studies made it appears that gull types can be roughly divided according to *Meinertzhagen* as done here. On this basis there is no evidence that Herring Gull occurs in the UAE, and is therefore not included.

Armenian Gull *Larus armenicus*

Common passage migrant and winter visitor. Regularly recorded offshore, where it may slightly outnumber Yellow-legged Gull in winter. Smaller numbers found inshore, and at lagoons, sewage plants and creeks. Many first-winter birds present, while adults resemble *taimyrensis/barabensis* in most respects except for the small head and short bill with a prominent dark band round the tip (also found in late immatures of the other species, which are however still likely to have some dark immature markings on the wing). Origins include the mountain lakes of Central Soviet Asia. – WV/PM

Note: This form is sometimes treated as a race of the Herring Gull, though it seems to be closer to the Lesser Black-backs, and it is still uncertain how they are best classified. See notes below texts of those species.

Gull-billed Tern *Gelochelidon nilotica*

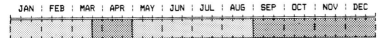

| JAN | FEB | MAR | APR | MAY | JUN | JUL | AUG | SEP | OCT | NOV | DEC |

A common passage migrant, found on creeks, sheltered lagoons and tidal pools. Sometimes on coasts though rarely at sea. Occurs throughout the year and is most common in April, and from September to December. Scarce May and June. Immatures are regularly recorded and can be confused with first-winter Sandwich Tern. Usually feeds by dipping to water surface or by taking insects in flight. A number of pairs nest on the Iranian side of the Gulf. – PM/wv/sv

Gull-billed Tern

Sandwich Tern

Sandwich Tern *Sterna sandvicensis*   Plate 8

| JAN | FEB | MAR | APR | MAY | JUN | JUL | AUG | SEP | OCT | NOV | DEC |

Common throughout the year along coasts, and on creeks and mudflats. Large numbers are present on passage and many congregate at mudflats, remote beaches and inland shallow pools. Nesting grounds lie outside the Middle East, and many spend their first summer in the Gulf, often forming colonies at inshore sites from May to early September. First-winter birds can be confused with Gull-billed Tern. – PM/WV/SV

Caspian Tern *Sterna caspia*

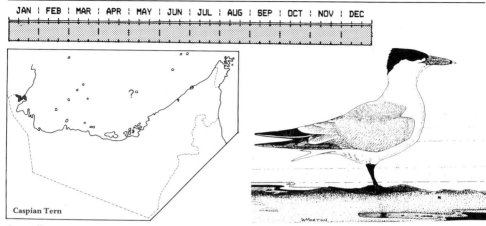

| JAN | FEB | MAR | APR | MAY | JUN | JUL | AUG | SEP | OCT | NOV | DEC |

Generally uncommon passage migrant and winter visitor, with small numbers present in summer. As the breeding season varies considerably with local conditions, it is recorded most of the year in the UAE. Central Asian populations appear to be present from August to March on sheltered lagoons, inshore islands and coasts, usually at roost and seldom in large numbers. Small numbers nest on islands in other parts of the Gulf, and it has nested at Khor al Udayd (near the Qatar border). Other nesting reports are unconfirmed. – wv/pm/rb?

Swift (Crested) Tern *Sterna bergii*   Plate 8

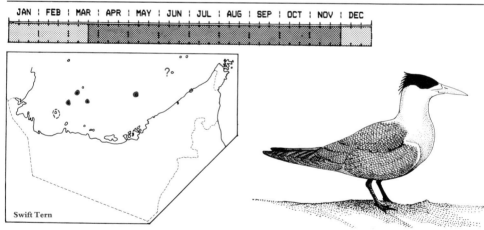

| JAN | FEB | MAR | APR | MAY | JUN | JUL | AUG | SEP | OCT | NOV | DEC |

Summer breeding visitor, some probably resident and dispersive. Most present from late March to November, though never common. Usually found far offshore, although also occurs in harbours and on beaches and creeks. Forms breeding colonies on Gulf islands, usually with Lesser Crested Tern, from April to late summer, eggs from early to mid May. Breeding is often unsuccessful due to disturbance, predation and egg-collectors. Most disperse by September. – MB/wv/rb

Note: Island breeding colonies are endangered and need protection.

Roseate Tern *Sterna dougallii*

Vagrant. One recorded off Ras al Khaimah on 23rd October 1986 and two reported off Jebel Ali on 10th May 1989. Considered likely stray to the Gulf of Oman (East Coast) from Indian Ocean breeding colonies. – V

Lesser Crested Tern *Sterna bengalensis*   Plate 8

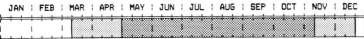

| JAN | FEB | MAR | APR | MAY | JUN | JUL | AUG | SEP | OCT | NOV | DEC |

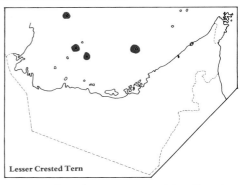

Lesser Crested Tern

Common summer breeding visitor forming large colonies on several Gulf islands from April. Egg-laying synchronised and spontaneous from mid May, often in company of larger Swift Tern. Disperses from late summer, and breeding sites vacated by September. Likely to occur along coasts and creeks, particularly on the East Coast where it occurs regularly, some even in winter. – MB

Little Tern *Sterna albifrons*

Scarce passage migrant, and probably overlooked due to prevalence of *S. saundersi* in region and difficulty of separating two in field. Reported from creeks and lagoons, sometimes inland. Nearest breeding areas include the Eastern Province of Saudi Arabia, southern Iranian wetlands and Khuzestan (Euphrates delta), where nesting has been reported April to June. No breeding recorded in the UAE. – pm

Saunders' Little Tern *Sterna saundersi*   Plate 8

| JAN | FEB | MAR | APR | MAY | JUN | JUL | AUG | SEP | OCT | NOV | DEC |

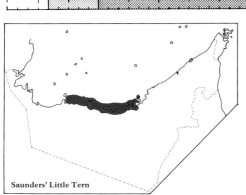

Saunders' Little Tern

Common breeding visitor and passage migrant along shorelines and creeks, sometimes at marshes and ponds near the coast. Most from April to October. Numerous over fish shoals in autumn, though scarce and localised in winter. Nests on inshore islands. Numbers also breed on Qatar, Bahrain and southern Iranian islands from April. Sometimes regarded as conspecific with Little Tern *S. albifrons* from which it is difficult to tell apart – PM/mb

Bridled Tern *Sterna anaethetus*

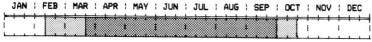

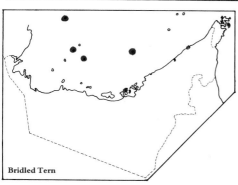

Bridled Tern

Widespread summer breeding visitor arriving in March (earlier some years), with numbers increasing at Gulf island nesting sites from late April. Nests May (eggs late May) to July in loose colonies. Generally the commonest tern found offshore in late summer. Disperses to tropical oceans from September, very few remaining over winter months. Roosts in mixed tern flocks on East Coast beaches. Often seen perched on buoys and other floats. Feeds far offshore by day, returning to landfall at night, when it is often active and calling. – MB

Sooty Tern *Sterna fuscata*

Scarce. Rarely reported in UAE territory and likely to be confused with Bridled Tern. Highly pelagic, and Gulf of Oman represents extreme north of range. Small numbers nest in June on Umm al Fayarrin Island, off the east coast of the Musandam Peninsula (Oman). – sv

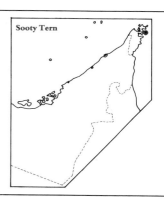

Sooty Tern

Common Tern *Sterna hirundo*

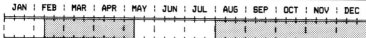

Uncommon passage migrant, most occurring August to September, occasionally to December. Also likely, though in smaller numbers, mid February to early May. Favours coasts and creeks, and nearby sewage works. Reported off East Coast in winter. Possibly under-recorded, as reports indicate confusion with White-cheeked Tern. – pm

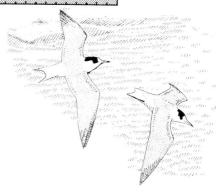

White-cheeked Tern *Sterna repressa* Plate 8

| JAN | FEB | MAR | APR | MAY | JUN | JUL | AUG | SEP | OCT | NOV | DEC |

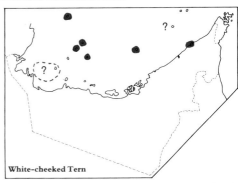

White-cheeked Tern

Common and widespread, breeding in large colonies from late April (eggs May to June) on some offshore islands. Disperses from late July when recorded inshore, on coasts, creeks and at communal roosts on quieter beaches, particularly on the East Coast. Occasionally first-winter birds occur further inland at sewage ponds and other areas of open water. Reportedly common offshore over fish shoals in winter, though generally scarce from mid November. – MB

Whiskered Tern *Chlidonias hybrida*

| JAN | FEB | MAR | APR | MAY | JUN | JUL | AUG | SEP | OCT | NOV | DEC |

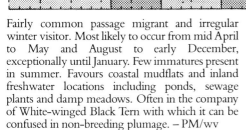

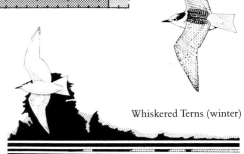

Fairly common passage migrant and irregular winter visitor. Most likely to occur from mid April to May and August to early December, exceptionally until January. Few immatures present in summer. Favours coastal mudflats and inland freshwater locations including ponds, sewage plants and damp meadows. Often in the company of White-winged Black Tern with which it can be confused in non-breeding plumage. – PM/wv

Whiskered Terns (winter)

White-winged Black Tern *Chlidonias leucopterus*

| JAN | FEB | MAR | APR | MAY | JUN | JUL | AUG | SEP | OCT | NOV | DEC |

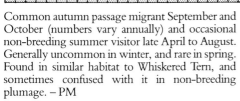

White-winged
Black Terns (winter)

Common autumn passage migrant September and October (numbers vary annually) and occasional non-breeding summer visitor late April to August. Generally uncommon in winter, and rare in spring. Found in similar habitat to Whiskered Tern, and sometimes confused with it in non-breeding plumage. – PM

Indian Skimmer *Rhynchops albicollis*

Vagrant to the Gulf of Oman, straying to the East Coast from more normal range around the Indian sub-continent. One occurred near Khor Kalba in January 1988. – V

Lichtenstein's Sandgrouse *Pterocles lichtensteinii*

JAN	FEB	MAR	APR	MAY	JUN	JUL	AUG	SEP	OCT	NOV	DEC

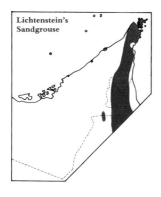

Common resident of hillsides, stony wadis and gravel plains. Rarely seen during the day except when flushed by chance on rocky slopes or open ground. Drinks at favoured pools (often in large numbers in summer) when best observed after sunset and before dawn, and usually identified by its call. Nests from April to September. – RB

Coronetted Sandgrouse *Pterocles coronatus*

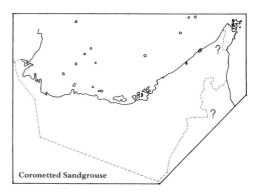

Breeding status uncertain, likely to be nomadic though very rarely seen. More reported in winter when it occurs on stony hillsides, gravel plains and wadis. Fairly common resident in Northern Oman. – rb?

Plate 9

41   *C. Gross / K. Hyland*

42   *C. Gross / K. Hyland*

43   *C. Gross / K. Hyland*

44   *D. Robinson*

45   *D. Robinson*

41. Barn Owl *Tyto alba*, near Dubai, spring 1986.   Text Page 116
42. Scops Owl *Otus scops*, near Dubai, mid October 1986.   " Page 116
43. Little Owl *Athene noctua* at nest-hole near Jebel Ali, February 1987.   " Page 118
44. Palm Dove *Streptopelia senegalensis*, Abu Dhabi, March 1990.   " Page 115
45. Rose-ringed Parakeet *Psittacula krameri* feeding on sunflower seeds, Abu Dhabi, March 1990.   " Page 115

Plate 10

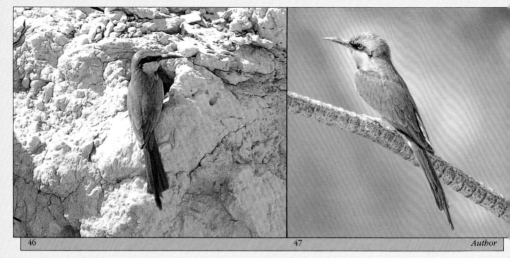

46

47

Author

48

C. Gross / K. Hyland

49

D. Robinson

50

Author

Plate 11

51   *Author*

54   *D. Robinson*

52   *Author*

53   *D. Robinson*

55   *Author*

Plate 12

56   *Author*

58   *Author*

59   *D. Robinson*

57   *Author*

60   *Author*

56. White-cheeked Bulbul *Pycnonotus leucogenys*, Jebel Ali Hotel grounds, June 1988.   Text Page 133
57. Crested Lark *Galerida cristata*, feeding on a Dubai roundabout, December 1989.   "   Page 126
58. Summer-plumaged Red-throated Pipit *Anthus cervinus*, Saffa Park, early May 1988.   "   Page 131
59. Tawny Pipit *Anthus campestris*, wintering in Dubai, early December 1989.   "   Page 129
60. First-winter Richard's Pipit *Anthus novaeseelandiae*, Dubai camel race track, mid October 1989.   "   Page 129

Plate 13

61 — D. Robinson

62 — D. Robinson

63 — D. Robinson

64 — Author

65 — M. West

61. Rufous Bush Chat *Cercotrichas galactotes*, Ras al Khaimah, early April 1990.　Text Page 135
62. Yellow-vented Bulbul *Pycnonotus xanthopygos*, Hatta, January 1990.　" Page 134
63. Male Black Redstart *Phoenicurus ochruros* (red-bellied race), Hatta, January 1990.　" Page 137
64. Female Redstart *Phoenicurus phoenicurus*, Qarnayn Island, late April 1989.　" Page 137
65. Male Redstart in Dubai garden.　" Page 137

Plate 14

66   M. West

68   D. Robinson

69   D. Robinson

67   D. Robinson

70   M. West

66. Isabelline Wheatear *Oenanthe isabellina*, in Saffa Park.   Text Page 138
67. Male Pied Wheatear *Oenanthe pleschanka*, near Al Ain, March 1990.   "   Page 139
68. First-summer Northern Wheatear *Oenanthe oenanthe,* gravel plains, near Al Ain, March 1990.   "   Page 138
69. Male Whinchat *Saxicola rubetra* on a date palm near Ras al Khaimah, early April 1990.   "   Page 137
70. Stonechat *Saxicola torquata*, wintering in Saffa Park 1984.   "   Page 138

Plate 15

71   *Author*

72   *D. Robinson*

73   74   *Author*

75   *Author*

76   *D. Robinson*

71.   Male Eastern Pied Wheatear *Oenanthe picata*, Qarn Nazwa, 10th November 1989
     (where it remained until following February)   Text Page 140
72.   Hume's Wheatear *Oenanthe alboniger*, in foothills near Al Ain, March 1990.   "   Page 141
73 &74.   Red-tailed Wheatear *Oenanthe xanthoprymna*, Qarn Nazwa, early November 1989.   "   Page 140
75.   Hume's Wheatear (probable juvenile) in grounds of Hatta Fort Hotel, early June 1989.   "   Page 141
76.   Male Black-eared Wheatear *Oenanthe hispanica* (white-throated form), Abu Dhabi, March 1990.   "   Page 139

Plate 16

77

M. West

79

D. Robinson

80

M. West

78

Author

81

M. West

Spotted Sandgrouse *Pterocles senegallus*

Uncommon and local, frequenting sandy scrub desert and gravel plains near foothills on the western side of the mountains. Possibly resident, though nesting details unknown, and rarely observed May to August. – rb?

Chestnut-bellied Sandgrouse *Pterocles exustus*

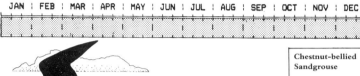

Fairly common breeding resident of foothills, gravel plains and desert (more likely to be seen away from the mountains than other sandgrouse species). In flight dark belly is very evident. Nests in late winter and early spring. Regularly reported from Kalba plain and nearby foothills. Has been observed feeding during the day in flocks of up to forty birds at water near Dubai, although status of urban birds are obscured by released and/or escaped individuals. – RB

Rock Dove *Columba livia*

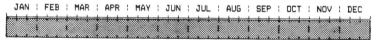

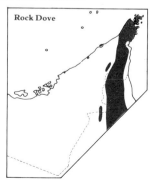

Fairly common breeding resident in most areas of the mountains and rocky outcrops, favouring steep hillsides and escarpments where few feral pigeons are likely to occur. Nests from March on ledges and in holes, sometimes under overhangs in rocky gorges. Difficult to distinguish from the domestic pigeon which has been introduced even to the most remote villages. – RB

Collared Dove *Streptopelia decaocto* Plate 8

| JAN | FEB | MAR | APR | MAY | JUN | JUL | AUG | SEP | OCT | NOV | DEC |

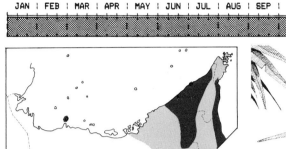

Collared Dove

Recent colonist and now a fairly widespread and locally abundant breeding resident, sometimes even displacing the ubiquitous Palm Dove in some areas. Peak nesting period from February to August. Partial and localised migration increases numbers in winter. Favours wooded areas and large gardens, requiring trees more than the Palm Dove. First colonised Arabia in 1963, though scarce in UAE prior to 1977. – RB/wv

Turtle Dove *Streptopelia turtur*

| JAN | FEB | MAR | APR | MAY | JUN | JUL | AUG | SEP | OCT | NOV | DEC |

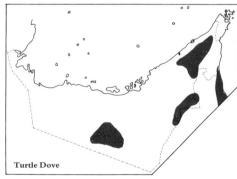

Turtle Dove

Fairly common passage migrant, and localised breeding visitor. Nests from May in semi-desert areas, favouring acacia plains near cultivations and villages. Common on passage April to May and mid August to early October, when it can occur in wooded parks and established large gardens, or wherever there are trees and drinking water. It feeds on the ground, often in the company of the resident Palm Dove. – PM/mb

Eastern Turtle Dove *Streptopelia orientalis*

Autumn vagrant from its normal, more eastern range. Reported October and November in Al Ain, Abu Dhabi and on Das Island. – V

Palm Dove *Streptopelia senegalensis* — Plate 9

JAN	FEB	MAR	APR	MAY	JUN	JUL	AUG	SEP	OCT	NOV	DEC

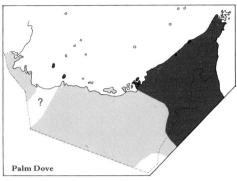

Palm Dove

Abundant breeding resident found almost everywhere, and able to tolerate even the most remote and inhospitable places, although most common in gardens and cultivations. Increasing in numbers as favoured habitat increases. Nests in nearly all months, especially late January to May. – RB

Field Note: Its unusual flight characteristics momentarily suggest totally unrelated species.

Namaqua Dove *Oena capensis*

Vagrant, though considered a prospective breeding visitor and future resident. First recorded in late May 1988 and 1989, at Asab in the southern desert interior, (where small numbers may already be resident). This dynamic coloniser is spreading its range from neighbouring states. – V

Rose-ringed Parakeet *Psittacula krameri* — Plate 9

JAN	FEB	MAR	APR	MAY	JUN	JUL	AUG	SEP	OCT	NOV	DEC

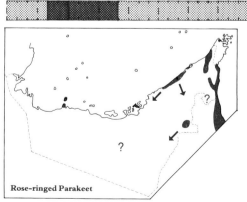

Rose-ringed Parakeet

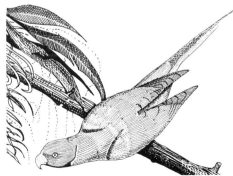

Common localised resident of gardens and cultivations, particularly in urban areas where it is often considered a pest. Occurs on passage February to April (and some may winter). Of rather mixed origin, this small Indian parrot has colonised many urban areas of the region, where its numbers are increasing rapidly. A popular ornamental cage bird, many escape or are introduced to the wild. Noisy and gregarious, it flies high at dusk, heading for roost. Nests from December, with a peak in March, and lays 4–6 eggs high in a tree hole or broken lamp post. – RB/pm

Cuckoo *Cuculus canorus*

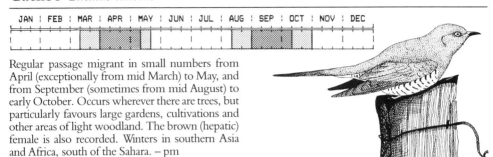

JAN	FEB	MAR	APR	MAY	JUN	JUL	AUG	SEP	OCT	NOV	DEC

Regular passage migrant in small numbers from April (exceptionally from mid March) to May, and from September (sometimes from mid August) to early October. Occurs wherever there are trees, but particularly favours large gardens, cultivations and other areas of light woodland. The brown (hepatic) female is also recorded. Winters in southern Asia and Africa, south of the Sahara. – pm

Indian Koel *Eudynamys scolopacea*

Vagrant from the Sub-continent. One recorded in Dubai 21-24th March 1977, and one in Abu Dhabi 16th February 1988. Strays have also been recorded in Oman and Iran. – V

Barn Owl *Tyto alba*   Plate 9

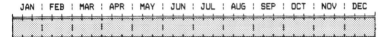

JAN	FEB	MAR	APR	MAY	JUN	JUL	AUG	SEP	OCT	NOV	DEC

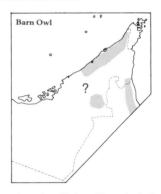

Barn Owl

Resident in very small numbers. Rarely seen, though probably widespread in semi-desert and open country near settlements. Hunts at night, and occasionally appears as a ghostly white creature in the glare of car headlights. Nests in holes of old buildings, often choosing the same nest site year after year, where it lays its 2-3 eggs between December and April. – rb

Scops Owl *Otus scops*   Plate 9

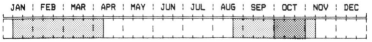

JAN	FEB	MAR	APR	MAY	JUN	JUL	AUG	SEP	OCT	NOV	DEC

A fairly common passage migrant mid January to early April and August to November, with a recorded peak in October. Often discovered by chance roosting in a tree by day, usually near habitation. Becomes active shortly after dusk. Feeds on night-flying insects and mice, though other small birds do occasionally fall prey to this tiny owl. Most birds occurring on passage likely to be from nesting grounds in the temperate forest zone of Central Soviet Asia, en route for African wintering grounds. – PM

Note: Much confusion with scarcer Striated Scops Owl *Otus brucei*, as separation can prove difficult in the field. Timings and distribution require further study.

Striated (Bruce's) Scops Owl *Otus brucei*

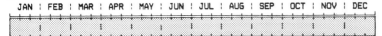

JAN	FEB	MAR	APR	MAY	JUN	JUL	AUG	SEP	OCT	NOV	DEC

Striated Scops Owl

Scarce breeding visitor found in cultivations, semi-desert with scattered trees, mountains and foothills.

Some may be resident, and most are reported in the Dubai area and the Northern Emirates. Nesting has been recorded in the Ras al Khaimah area in April. Reports show confusion with *Otus scops*. – mb/rb?

Eagle Owl *Bubo bubo*

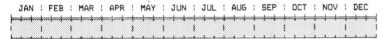

JAN	FEB	MAR	APR	MAY	JUN	JUL	AUG	SEP	OCT	NOV	DEC

Eagle Owl
(desert form)

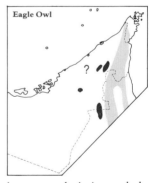

Eagle Owl

Scarce breeding resident of remote areas, including hillsides, escarpments and rocky outcrops, while some favour more open desert (with scattered *ghaf* trees for cover). A large and impressive bird, but sadly much persecuted. Active at dusk, it hunts rodents and small mammals. Nests from December, in caves and sheltered crevices. Its barking call is quite distinctive. – rb

Long-eared Owl *Asio otus*

Vagrant. Only a handful of sightings since 1970, from October to March, notably at Dubai, Sharjah and offshore Khor Fakkan (landed on board a ship). Can be confused with Short-eared Owl. – V

Short-eared Owl *Asio flammeus*

JAN	FEB	MAR	APR	MAY	JUN	JUL	AUG	SEP	OCT	NOV	DEC

An uncommon winter visitor, rarely seen by day, although it has been found in unusual places on migration including ships and offshore islands. Passage has been recorded from mid October and it may be present until mid March. Hunts in open country. When aware of danger it raises its ear tufts in a similar manner to Long-eared Owl. – wv

Little Owl *Athene noctua* Plate 9

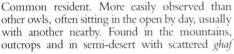

| JAN | FEB | MAR | APR | MAY | JUN | JUL | AUG | SEP | OCT | NOV | DEC |

Little Owl

Common resident. More easily observed than other owls, often sitting in the open by day, usually with another nearby. Found in the mountains, outcrops and in semi-desert with scattered *ghaf* trees. Nests from February to May, laying 3–6 eggs. Pale and brown forms of *A. n. saharae* are regularly recorded. – rb

---

European Nightjar *Caprimulgus europaeus* Plate 10

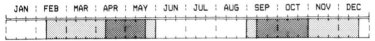

| JAN | FEB | MAR | APR | MAY | JUN | JUL | AUG | SEP | OCT | NOV | DEC |

Irregular migrant, recorded in April, May, mid September to early November and occasionally in winter months. Prefers lightly wooded areas where it roosts by day. May allow close approach. It has a widespread breeding range from Europe to India, occurring in the Southern Gulf on passage to Africa. Smaller and paler Iranian sub-species *C. e. unwini*, is likely to occur. Should not be confused with the pale rufous Egyptian Nightjar (scarce). – PM

Egyptian Nightjar *Caprimulgus aegyptius*

| JAN | FEB | MAR | APR | MAY | JUN | JUL | AUG | SEP | OCT | NOV | DEC |

Very scarce passage migrant March, April, August to October, and occasionally in other months. Likely to favour more arid areas than European Nightjar, although some have been reported resting on ships on passage. – pm

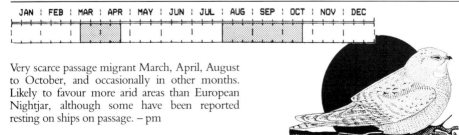

Common Swift *Apus apus*

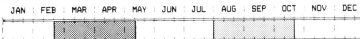

JAN	FEB	MAR	APR	MAY	JUN	JUL	AUG	SEP	OCT	NOV	DEC

Fairly common spring passage migrant, late February (occasionally earlier) to May, often over damp meadows, ponds and sewage farms. Quite scarce on its southerly autumn passage, but at all times is much confused with Pallid Swift, which is present in sizeable numbers in many areas from November to June. The paler eastern race *A. a. pekinensis* is likely to occur. – PM

Pallid Swift *Apus pallidus*

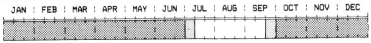

JAN	FEB	MAR	APR	MAY	JUN	JUL	AUG	SEP	OCT	NOV	DEC

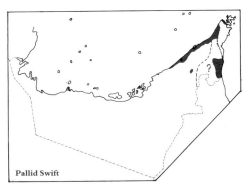

Pallid Swift

Common breeding visitor and passage migrant October to June. Scarce July to late September. The paler tones of its plumage are difficult to ascertain in the field, especially compared with pale races of Common Swift. Nests in colonies, with peak activity December to March. Congregates in large numbers at dusk at favoured sites, particularly around Dubai Museum (the city's old fort). – MB/pm

Alpine Swift *Apus melba*

Vagrant or very scarce and irregular passage migrant, with less than ten sightings since 1975. Records include single birds in April, May, August and October most in the Dubai area. – V

Little Swift *Apus affinis*

Vagrant, with less than a handful of records of single birds January to March in a number of locations. Once in July in Sharjah. Normally sedentary in its southern breeding range, which includes southern Arabia and Iran. – V

White-collared Kingfisher *Halcyon chloris*

JAN ¦ FEB ¦ MAR ¦ APR ¦ MAY ¦ JUN ¦ JUL ¦ AUG ¦ SEP ¦ OCT ¦ NOV ¦ DEC

White-collared
Kingfisher

An isolated colony is resident at an area of tidal mangroves on the East Coast. Often seen at low tide when it hunts for crabs on the exposed mudflats, or when perching prominently on low tree branches. Its presence often revealed by its rattling alarm call. Recorded at nest holes April to June, though little other breeding information available. The local sub-species is endangered, due to disturbance and habitat destruction. – rb

Kingfisher *Alcedo atthis*

JAN ¦ FEB ¦ MAR ¦ APR ¦ MAY ¦ JUN ¦ JUL ¦ AUG ¦ SEP ¦ OCT ¦ NOV ¦ DEC

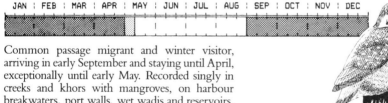

Common passage migrant and winter visitor, arriving in early September and staying until April, exceptionally until early May. Recorded singly in creeks and khors with mangroves, on harbour breakwaters, port walls, wet wadis and reservoirs. During passage, widespread and often seen at inland ponds and lakes. – WV/PM

Pied Kingfisher *Ceryle rudis*

JAN ¦ FEB ¦ MAR ¦ APR ¦ MAY ¦ JUN ¦ JUL ¦ AUG ¦ SEP ¦ OCT ¦ NOV ¦ DEC

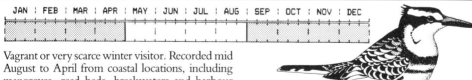

Vagrant or very scarce winter visitor. Recorded mid August to April from coastal locations, including mangroves, reed beds, breakwaters and harbour walls. Breeding grounds include the Tigris and Euphrates deltas at the head of the Arabian Gulf, where it is normally sedentary. – V/wv?

White-throated Bee-eater *Merops albicollis*

Vagrant. One adult occurred at the Emirates golf course on 20th November 1989, and another was found there on 5th March 1990. Probably the most northerly records of this mainly African species, whose nearest breeding grounds lie around the southern tip of the Arabian peninsula. – V

Little Green Bee-eater *Merops orientalis*

Plate 10

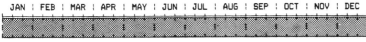

Common resident, now extending its breeding range further south and west. It has spread to most parts of the Northern Emirates aon resident, now extending its breeding range further south and west. It has spread to most parts of the Northern Emirates and Hajar mountains, where it favours sheltered wadis, cultivations and semi-desert with scattered acacia trees. The region's only resident bee-eater, often found in small flocks sitting on exposed branches or power cables and can be quite tame. Excavates its nest hole in mudbanks and wadi sides laying its eggs from April (occasionally from February) to June, and reported at nest holes from November. Local race *M. o. muscatensis* has blue throat and supercilium, but juveniles are generally duller, and throat can be pale yellow. – RB

Blue-cheeked Bee-eater *Merops superciliosus*

Plate 10

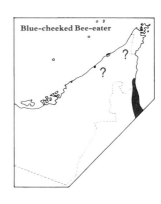

Common autumn migrant from late August to early November often in large feeding flocks. Spring passage is more erratic, extended and over a broad front, from February with a peak April to mid May. Irregular and localised breeding visitor, nesting late April or May, favouring open country with scattered high trees, usually around cultivations and close to water. Breeding first noted near Fujeirah in 1989, when juveniles were present in late June. Most likely to be seen feeding at high level over cultivations and savannah plain, perching on power cables and tall trees in favoured locations. – PM/mb

European Bee-eater *Merops apiaster* — Plate 10

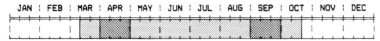

| JAN | FEB | MAR | APR | MAY | JUN | JUL | AUG | SEP | OCT | NOV | DEC |

European Bee-eater

A fairly common and regular migrant, from March to May, and August to mid October, often in large flocks in April and September. Localised breeding visitor, nesting from May (occasionally earlier) near cultivations, palm plantations, and open country with scattered high trees, close to water and near suitable banks for nest holes. A breeding site at Digdaga, near Ras al Khaimah was confirmed in 1989, and others may yet be discovered. Call usually heard before birds seen, often in high circling flocks. Perches quite prominently on tall trees, even on roof aerials, and may linger in favoured locations such as parks, gardens and cultivations for several days on passage. – PM/mb

Wryneck *Jynx torquilla*

| JAN | FEB | MAR | APR | MAY | JUN | JUL | AUG | SEP | OCT | NOV | DEC |

Regular passage migrant and irregular winter visitor. Most likely from March to early April, and from September (some years from August) to October, and is usually solitary. Favours woodland, parks, gardens, cultivations and other areas with scattered trees and shade. On passage often found by chance and seldom remains long at one location. – pm/wv

European Roller *Coracias garrulus* — Plate 11

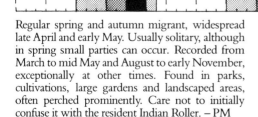

| JAN | FEB | MAR | APR | MAY | JUN | JUL | AUG | SEP | OCT | NOV | DEC |

Regular spring and autumn migrant, widespread late April and early May. Usually solitary, although in spring small parties can occur. Recorded from March to mid May and August to early November, exceptionally at other times. Found in parks, cultivations, large gardens and landscaped areas, often perched prominently. Care not to initially confuse it with the resident Indian Roller. – PM

Indian Roller *Coracias benghalensis*   Plate 11

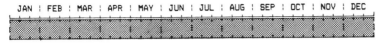

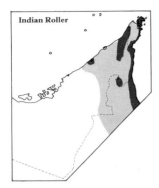

Common resident of wadis, cultivations and mountain villages, often associated with palm plantations. Presently recorded throughout the year in most northern and eastern areas of the country, where it is becoming more widespread, colonising parks and large gardens on the Arabian Gulf coast. Records in Dubai show an increase mid August to December and reports from offshore islands in January and March indicate seasonal movements. Perches prominently on trees, lamp-posts and power cables. Nests in tree holes and rock cavities from January and disperses from June. – RB/pm?

Hoopoe *Upupa epops*   Plate 11

Common and widespread passage migrant and winter visitor. Summer visitors, plus a likely resident population, breed in variable numbers annually. The nest, in a rock cavity or tree hole is occupied from April to June. Migrants are widespread, favouring lightly wooded parkland, large gardens and other areas of open country with trees. Peak passage mid February to early April and late August to October. Sometimes feeds in small loose flocks. Rarely recorded in the mountains. – PM/wv/mb/rb?

Black-crowned Finch Lark *Eremopterix nigriceps*   Plate 11

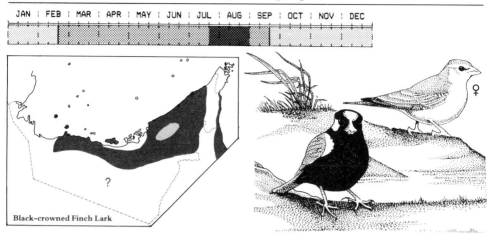

| JAN | FEB | MAR | APR | MAY | JUN | JUL | AUG | SEP | OCT | NOV | DEC |

Black-crowned Finch Lark

Common breeding resident, though majority move away from breeding areas, particularly coasts, in winter. Nests March to July in areas of desert scrub, savannah and flat plains, often near cultivations or acacia groves. Flocks gather from mid July to September at favoured sites near water until completion of moult. Movements are not really understood but local populations appear to be partial migrants, wandering outside the breeding season. Many move inland in winter. – RB

Desert Lark *Ammomanes deserti*   Plate 11

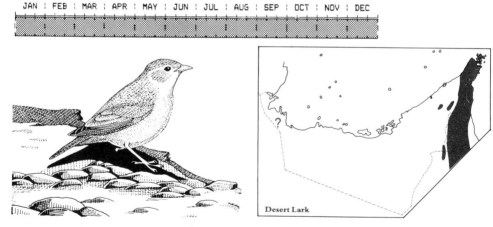

| JAN | FEB | MAR | APR | MAY | JUN | JUL | AUG | SEP | OCT | NOV | DEC |

Desert Lark

Very common breeding resident rarely found away from rocky wadis, gravel plains and broken hillsides. Often the only species to be seen (and heard) in remote mountain areas. Occasionally wanders to nearby gravel plains to feed in small parties. Isolated groups have colonised rocky outcrops away from the main mountain range. Records on Gulf islands in winter and spring indicate a more widespread dispersal. Nesting reported from April, with eggs June. Race found in mountains (believed *A. d. phoenicuroides*) has rufous-buff tinges to wings and flanks, which are distinctive and visible in flight. – RB

Hoopoe (Bifasciated) Lark *Alaemon alaudipes*

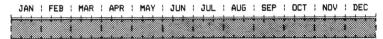

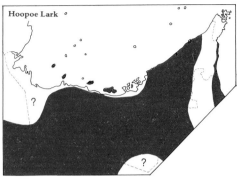

Hoopoe Lark

Widespread breeding resident of coastal dunes, inland desert and sabkha scrub, sometimes found even in the most remote sand dunes of the interior, but not in the mountains. Largest lark of the region and often located by its distinctive display flight and mournful call. An early breeder, with young recorded at the nest in February. Distributed widely across north Africa and the deserts of the Middle East. – RB

Bimaculated Lark *Melanocorypha bimaculata*

Very rare autumn migrant with only a few recent records. Most have occurred in October and November, when immature birds can be overlooked or misidentified. Also recorded in February and April. – V.

Short-toed Lark *Calandrella brachydactyla*

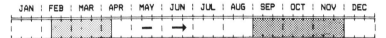

Fairly common passage migrant, sometimes in sizeable flocks, from early September to November, occasionally in winter. Northerly passage February to April is quite variable. Breeding behaviour noted near Umm al Quwain, May 1990. Favours stony plains, flat coastal scrub and irrigated grassland. Care should be taken to distinguish it from Lesser Short-toed Lark. – PM/cb?

Note: Irregular spring influxes (often in hundreds) recorded in Bahrain and nearby Hawar islands. Also a casual breeder in some other neighbouring regions, including Northern Oman.

Lesser Short-toed Lark *Calandrella rufescens*

JAN	FEB	MAR	APR	MAY	JUN	JUL	AUG	SEP	OCT	NOV	DEC

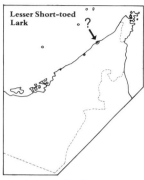

Scarce passage migrant and localised winter visitor, found on sandy semi-desert, salt marsh scrub and less often, on open grassy landscaped areas. Passage recorded mid September to November and March to mid April. Small flocks have occurred, particularly in winter. May occur in other months. Nesting behaviour has been reported in late April on Siniyah Island. – pm/wv/mb?

Crested Lark *Galerida cristata* — Plate 12

JAN	FEB	MAR	APR	MAY	JUN	JUL	AUG	SEP	OCT	NOV	DEC

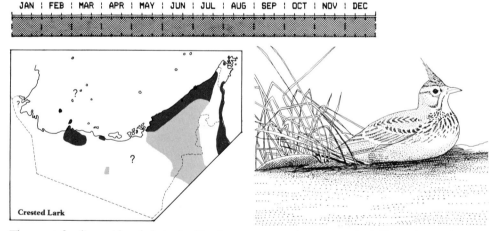

The most familiar resident lark in the Northern Emirates, found on open cultivation, grassed parks, roadsides, large gardens and semi-desert, though rarely far from sandy areas or coastal plains. Some have colonised new cultivated areas in remote desert areas (and Sir Bani Yas Island) to south and west. Gregarious and quite tame, nesting from January to May laying up to 5 eggs in a shaded hollow or tussock of grass. – RB

Temminck's Horned Lark *Eremophila bilopha*

Vagrant from normally sedentary range in north-western Arabia. One was reported in Jumeirah, Dubai in December 1982. –V

Skylark *Alauda arvensis*

JAN	FEB	MAR	APR	MAY	JUN	JUL	AUG	SEP	OCT	NOV	DEC

Common winter visitor from the last week in October to early March (stragglers to early April some years). Wintering numbers (often in flocks of 20 or more together) have increased in recent times, a response to the new grassed areas such as playing fields, golf courses and public parks. Also likely to occur in fertile scrub and cultivations, usually near the coast. The Arabian peninsula is the southern limit of wintering range, from nesting grounds in north-eastern Europe and central Russia. – WV

Sand Martin *Riparia riparia*

JAN	FEB	MAR	APR	MAY	JUN	JUL	AUG	SEP	OCT	NOV	DEC

Fairly common and widespread on spring and autumn passage, with small numbers overwintering. Most occur from late August to early October and late March to May, occasionally present in June and July. No breeding has been reported. Often accompanies other hirundines on migration, near cultivations, parks and sewage works. – PM/wv

Pale Crag Martin *Hirundo obsoleta*

JAN	FEB	MAR	APR	MAY	JUN	JUL	AUG	SEP	OCT	NOV	DEC

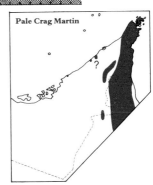

Pale Crag Martin

Common breeding resident of wadis, gravel plains, hills, seacliffs and rocky outcrops, often near habitation. Usually seen in pairs or small parties, although large flocks congregate over cultivations and other favoured sites including west coastal plain within sight of the mountains in winter. Nests from February to April, beneath rock overhangs, at waterfalls and ravines, in caves and under the eaves of buildings. Small numbers nest away from the mountains. – RB

Note: Considered by some as a race of African Rock Martin *Ptyonoprogne fuligula* (not listed).

Crag Martin *Ptyonoprogne rupestris*

JAN	FEB	MAR	APR	MAY	JUN	JUL	AUG	SEP	OCT	NOV	DEC

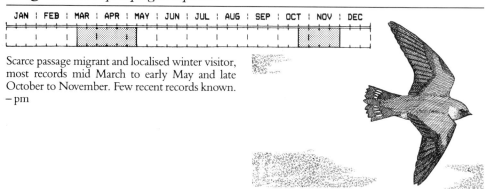

Scarce passage migrant and localised winter visitor, most records mid March to early May and late October to November. Few recent records known. – pm

Swallow *Hirundo rustica*

JAN	FEB	MAR	APR	MAY	JUN	JUL	AUG	SEP	OCT	NOV	DEC

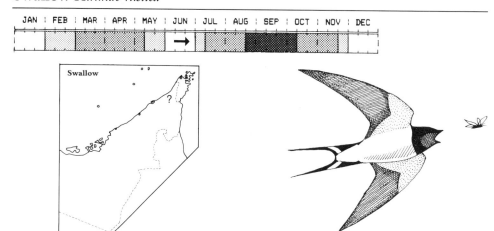

Common spring and autumn migrant, occasionally at other times. Passes through in steady numbers northward from February to May and southward from July to November. Bred once at Khasab, Musandam, and small numbers may nest in the Ras al Khaimah area, where suitable farm habitat exists. May linger for days in small flocks, occasionally with other hirundines at cultivations, large landscaped gardens and moist areas, otherwise widespread almost everywhere. – PM/cb?

Red-rumped Swallow *Hirundo daurica*

JAN	FEB	MAR	APR	MAY	JUN	JUL	AUG	SEP	OCT	NOV	DEC

Uncommon passage migrant February to April (occasionally to early May) generally peaking in March. Few late September and early October, rare at other times. As with other hirundines, most likely to be seen over sewage treatment plants, rubbish tips, damp landscaped areas and cultivations, though may occur almost anywhere on passage. The rump and collar appear pale buff on most birds in the field. – pm

House Martin *Delichon urbica*

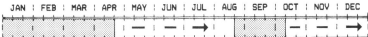

| JAN | FEB | MAR | APR | MAY | JUN | JUL | AUG | SEP | OCT | NOV | DEC |

Irregular passage migrant, found singly or in small parties (though large influxes can occur some years), from January to April and late August to early October. Some also recorded in summer and winter months, when it may associate with Pale Crag Martin. Usually favours damp areas, including sewage works, ponds, rubbish dumps and irrigated grassland. – pm

Richard's Pipit *Anthus novaeseelandiae* Plate 12

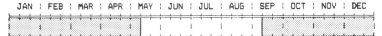

| JAN | FEB | MAR | APR | MAY | JUN | JUL | AUG | SEP | OCT | NOV | DEC |

Uncommon and irregular passage migrant and occasional winter visitor, found singly or in small parties from mid September to early May. Occurs on grassy areas, scrub and cultivations, and can be quite wary. Its upright stance and distinctive face markings assist in field identification, though records show confusion with juvenile Tawny Pipits. Confusion is also likely with Blyth's Pipit *A. godlewskii* (see page 169). – pm/wv

Tawny Pipit *Anthus campestris* Plate 12

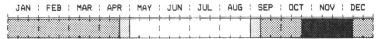

| JAN | FEB | MAR | APR | MAY | JUN | JUL | AUG | SEP | OCT | NOV | DEC |

Common passage migrant and winter visitor from September to mid April. During peak passage from late October to early December it can be common and often in groups, in parks, rubbish dumps, open grassland, desert scrub and cultivations. Some 1st-winter birds can retain streaking on breast and back well into autumn (though most juveniles moult in late summer), and they should not be confused with Richard's Pipit. (See also Long-billed Pipit and Blyth's Pipit). – PM/WV

Long-billed Pipit *Anthus similis*

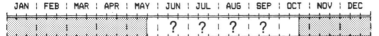

JAN	FEB	MAR	APR	MAY	JUN	JUL	AUG	SEP	OCT	NOV	DEC
				?	?	?	?				

Scarce winter visitor late October to April (occasionally to May) to coastal plains and scrub, possibly members of Iranian breeding populations. Also recorded on Arabian Gulf islands. Suspected of breeding in mountain areas, where reported in song in February, though no nests discovered and further study is needed. Large size and longer bill help to distinguish it from Tawny Pipit. – wv/rb?

Olive-backed Pipit *Anthus hodgsoni*

Vagrant. Single birds reported in November and December (and once in March) less than a handful of times since first documented sighting in 1973.

Usual wintering range is from India to the Phillipines. – V

Tree Pipit *Anthus trivialis*

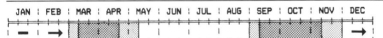

JAN	FEB	MAR	APR	MAY	JUN	JUL	AUG	SEP	OCT	NOV	DEC
—	→									→	

Common and regular passage migrant, found in parks, gardens and open grassland with scattered trees from March to early May and from September to November. Small numbers may overwinter some years. Often in loose parties, feeding in shaded areas. More approachable than similar Meadow Pipit and more likely to be associated with trees. – PM

Pechora Pipit *Anthus gustavi*

Vagrant, one was observed near the road to Jebel Dhanna, 50 kilometres west of Abu Dhabi on 4th

November 1988. Normal wintering range includes the Far East. – V

Meadow Pipit *Anthus pratensis*

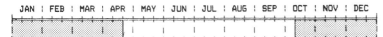

JAN	FEB	MAR	APR	MAY	JUN	JUL	AUG	SEP	OCT	NOV	DEC

Uncommon winter visitor from mid October (earlier some years) to mid April, when it can be found in a variety of habitats including parks, damp ditches, cultivations and coastal scrub. Sometimes confused with Red-throated Pipit in autumn and winter, and Tree Pipit in spring and autumn. Tends to be wary and easily disturbed. Triple "seep" call distinctive. – wv

Red-throated Pipit *Anthus cervinus* Plate 12

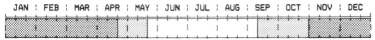

JAN	FEB	MAR	APR	MAY	JUN	JUL	AUG	SEP	OCT	NOV	DEC

A fairly common passage migrant and localised winter visitor. Most likely to be found November to April (occasionally September, October and May). Rather irregular in winter months, though usually in small sedentary flocks at favoured sites. Favours damp lawns, wet hollows and surface water margins. Red throat colouring spring and autumn only. – PM/wv

Water Pipit *Anthus spinoletta*

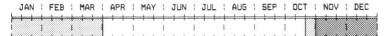

JAN	FEB	MAR	APR	MAY	JUN	JUL	AUG	SEP	OCT	NOV	DEC

Scarce and irregular winter visitor, more likely to be found in November and December, less frequently to March, and usually in small numbers. Feeds in mixed pipit and wagtail flocks, on grassland, large open gardens, and at sewage works and water treatment plants. Has been recorded as early as August and as late as April. – wv

Forest Wagtail *Dendronanthus indicus*

Rare winter visitor, single birds reported November 1987 in Bateen Wood, and one each 27th November 1989 in Bu Hasa and 6th December at Shah, south of Liwa. A surprising arrival from more-favoured Far Eastern wintering grounds. No other records known in Arabia. – V

Yellow Wagtail *Motacilla flava*

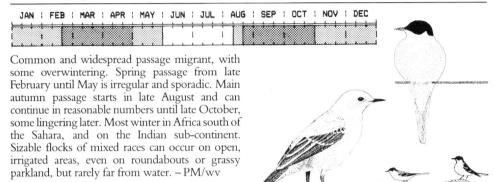

JAN	FEB	MAR	APR	MAY	JUN	JUL	AUG	SEP	OCT	NOV	DEC

Common and widespread passage migrant, with some overwintering. Spring passage from late February until May is irregular and sporadic. Main autumn passage starts in late August and can continue in reasonable numbers until late October, some lingering later. Most winter in Africa south of the Sahara, and on the Indian sub-continent. Sizable flocks of mixed races can occur on open, irrigated areas, even on roundabouts or grassy parkland, but rarely far from water. – PM/wv

Citrine Wagtail *Motacilla citreola*

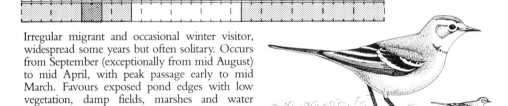

JAN	FEB	MAR	APR	MAY	JUN	JUL	AUG	SEP	OCT	NOV	DEC

Irregular migrant and occasional winter visitor, widespread some years but often solitary. Occurs from September (exceptionally from mid August) to mid April, with peak passage early to mid March. Favours exposed pond edges with low vegetation, damp fields, marshes and water treatment plants. – pm/wv

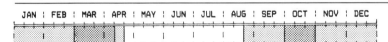

Grey Wagtail *Motacilla cinerea*

JAN	FEB	MAR	APR	MAY	JUN	JUL	AUG	SEP	OCT	NOV	DEC

Regular passage migrant and scarce winter visitor late August to mid April, though rarely seen in large numbers. Most common March to early April and October, at freshwater pool margins, wet grassland and some sewage works. Winters November to February in mountain wadis, near perennial streams. – PM/wv

White Wagtail *Motacilla alba*

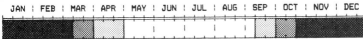

JAN	FEB	MAR	APR	MAY	JUN	JUL	AUG	SEP	OCT	NOV	DEC

Very common winter visitor, some from mid September, with a major influx from late October. Main departure late March, with stragglers remaining to end of April. Found in parks, large gardens, cultivations, sewage works, and on roundabouts and grassed verges. Prefers damp grass and other suitable habitat where there is an abundance of insects. Flocks at dusk to favoured roosts. – WV

Hypocolius *Hypocolius ampelinus*

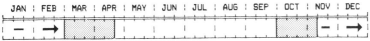

JAN	FEB	MAR	APR	MAY	JUN	JUL	AUG	SEP	OCT	NOV	DEC

Very scarce passage migrant. Most pass further west from Iranian breeding areas to favoured wintering areas in central Arabia (and Bahrain). Has been recorded March to mid April, and October to early November, and may winter locally (including Dalma Island). Favours cultivations, plantations and lightly wooded scrub. – pm/wv?

White-cheeked Bulbul *Pycnonotus leucogenys*   Plate 12

JAN	FEB	MAR	APR	MAY	JUN	JUL	AUG	SEP	OCT	NOV	DEC

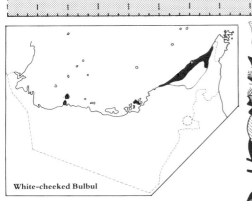

White-cheeked Bulbul

Uncommon resident of Gulf coastal towns and cultivations, currently spreading inland. Occurs in gardens and wooded grounds of hotels, parks and landscaped areas. Common on Abu Dhabi island. Interbreeds with Red-vented Bulbul, when 'orange-vented', or dark cheeked hybrids may result. Nests from May to July. A popular cage-bird, the presence of some at least are due to escapees or introduction in some areas. – rb

Yellow-vented Bulbul *Pycnonotus xanthopygos*   Plate 13

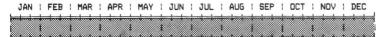

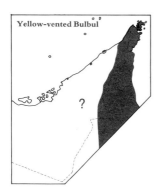

Breeding resident, most common in wadis and ravines of the mountains, and in gardens and cultivations of the adjacent gravel plains and east coastal belt, where it feeds on fruit and insects. Often active and in groups, its distinctive liquid call betrays its presence. Nests from February, eggs March. Also known as Black-capped Bulbul, and regarded formerly as conspecific with Common Bulbul. – RB

Note: Reports from gardens near Abu Dhabi, Dubai and Sharjah generally of dark-cheeked/yellow-vented hybrids of *P. leucogenys/cafer*.

Red-vented Bulbul *Pycnonotus cafer*

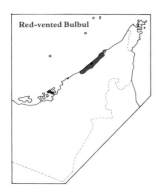

An introduced Indian species and now a breeding resident in suburban gardens of the Arabian Gulf coastal belt from Sharjah to Abu Dhabi. Occurs in a similar range and habitat to White-cheeked Bulbul with which it sometimes hybridises, resulting in a variety of mixed characteristics. Noisy and gregarious, favouring gardens and parks, rarely straying far from the coast. Perches prominently. Nests from May to July. – RB

Rufous Bush Chat *Cercotrichas galactotes*

Plate 13

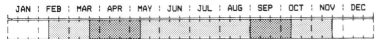

Rather elusive passage migrant and scarce breeding visitor found in dense woodland, cultivations, acacia scrub and other places with sufficient cover. Common on spring passage late March to early May and in smaller numbers September to early October. Early and late individuals recorded February and November. Reported on breeding territory from April, with young present in July. Few nest sites are known, and may be more widespread outside the towns than records suggest. – pm/mb

Note: Often in drier habitat than Nightingale, with which it is sometimes confused.

Thrush Nightingale *Luscinia luscinia*

A scarce passage migrant found in thick damp undergrowth and overgrown pond edges with sufficient cover. Most records late April to early May, less frequent September and October. Likely to be confused with Nightingale. – pm

Nightingale *Luscinia megarhynchos*

Plate 12

Fairly common passage migrant late March to May. Rather scarce late August to early October. Prefers moist areas, and is regularly found in ditches, damp thickets, low bushes and fallen trees. Confusion is possible with Thrush Nightingale. Regularly heard in song in spring, though no breeding has been reported. – PM

Robin *Erithacus rubecula*

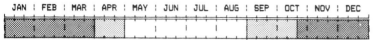

Very scarce winter visitor from November to January (to March some years) and is most likely to be found in thickets, woodland and overgrown vegetation where available. The lack of suitable habitat probably limits the numbers likely to occur. Not yet reported on the East Coast. – wv

Bluethroat *Luscinia svecica*

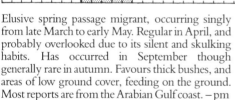

Common passage migrant and winter visitor. Light movement from September, with larger influx of winter visitors in late October. Skulks in damp undergrowth, ponds with border cover, low hedges, reed beds and large irrigated gardens and cultivations. Both white-spotted and red-spotted forms occur, though many immatures are present in autumn. Wintering birds depart in March, and in April there is irregular passage of the all-blue throated Caucasian race. – WV/PM

Bluethroat (1st winter)

White-throated Robin *Irania gutturalis*

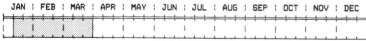

Elusive spring passage migrant, occurring singly from late March to early May. Regular in April, and probably overlooked due to its silent and skulking habits. Has occurred in September though generally rare in autumn. Favours thick bushes, and areas of low ground cover, feeding on the ground. Most reports are from the Arabian Gulf coast. – pm

Eversmann's Redstart *Phoenicurus erythronotus*

Very scarce and infrequent winter visitor. Most records mid January to March, though it has been reported in November on Das Island. Favours semi-desert with scattered trees, palm groves, cultivations and coastal scrub. – wv

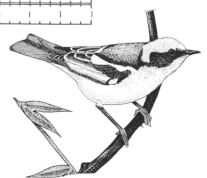

Black Redstart *Phoenicurus ochruros* — Plate 13

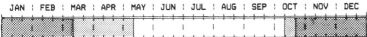

| JAN | FEB | MAR | APR | MAY | JUN | JUL | AUG | SEP | OCT | NOV | DEC |

Fairly common and widespread winter visitor from the end of October to early March, stragglers occasionally to early May. Occurs in shaded gardens, woodland, hillsides with scattered trees and acacia scrub. Eastern red-bellied male *P. o. phoenicuroides* is widespread (though other forms do occur), and it is sometimes confused with Redstart *P. phoenicurus* in early spring. – WV

Redstart *Phoenicurus phoenicurus* — Plate 13

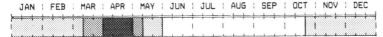

| JAN | FEB | MAR | APR | MAY | JUN | JUL | AUG | SEP | OCT | NOV | DEC |

Common and widespread spring passage migrant from mid March to early May (females occasionally present to late May). Generally rare in autumn. Irregular and localised in winter when individuals have been reported late October to February. Common in gardens, parks and other light woodland on passage. Males prevail to mid April. Sub-species *P. p. samamisicus* is regularly recorded from mid to late March and in October, the male distinguished by its white wing markings. – PM/wv

samamisicus

Whinchat *Saxicola rubetra* — Plate 14

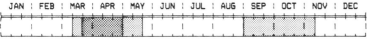

| JAN | FEB | MAR | APR | MAY | JUN | JUL | AUG | SEP | OCT | NOV | DEC |

Uncommon passage migrant from March to May and September (occasionally from August) to early November. Occasionally reported in winter months, particularly from mid January. Usually solitary and favours gardens, parkland, cultivations and semi-desert scrub, perching low, and sometimes hunting from ground level. – pm

Note: Sometimes confused with pale-headed 'Siberian' race of Stonechat which can occur April and September.

Stonechat *Saxicola torquata* — Plate 14

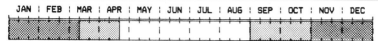

Fairly common, though localised winter visitor mostly from November to early March (small numbers from late October). Irregular passage of eastern race 'Siberian' Stonechats occur in September and April, many of which winter in north-east Africa. Found in fairly dry scrub, park edges and semi-arid desert and often overwinters in pairs. – wv/pm

Isabelline Wheatear *Oenanthe isabellina* — Plate 14

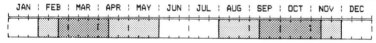

The commonest wintering wheatear in many areas. Present from the start of passage in mid August until mid April, peaking in November. As early as July some years, and stragglers can remain to May. Found in semi-desert, cultivations and parkland, though rarely in very arid areas. As with most wheatears the identification of autumn/winter plumaged and immature birds requires careful consideration. – PM/WV

Northern Wheatear *Oenanthe oenanthe* — Plate 14

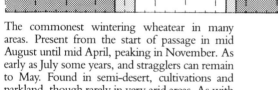

♂ Northern Wheatears

Common on spring passage late February to April (exceptionally to May). Less frequent in autumn, small numbers occurring mid September (from late July some years) to early November. Occasionally December and January, though traditional wintering grounds are further south. Favours open country with suitable perches, including coastal dunes, sabkha scrub, semi-desert, parks and cultivations. – PM

Pied Wheatear *Oenanthe pleschanka* — Plate 14

JAN	FEB	MAR	APR	MAY	JUN	JUL	AUG	SEP	OCT	NOV	DEC

Common spring passage migrant February to April, generally peaking in March. Uncommon mid September to early November (when most are in first winter plumage) and a few may overwinter some years. Very active, it occurs in a variety of locations including parks, acacia plains and desert scrub. Sometimes in mountain locations, when care should be taken not to mistake it for the similar, though scarce Mourning Wheatear. Pale-throated 'vittata' form has been recorded in spring. – PM

Black-eared Wheatear *Oenanthe hispanica* — Plate 15

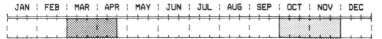

JAN	FEB	MAR	APR	MAY	JUN	JUL	AUG	SEP	OCT	NOV	DEC

Uncommon spring migrant March to mid April. Also recorded in October and November, though generally rare in autumn. Found at rubbish dumps, in bare open country with scattered trees and on coastal dunes. Black-throated form of pale race *O. h. melanoleuca* most frequently recorded. – pm

Desert Wheatear *Oenanthe deserti*

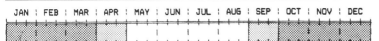

JAN	FEB	MAR	APR	MAY	JUN	JUL	AUG	SEP	OCT	NOV	DEC

Common winter visitor to semi-desert, sabkha scrub and coastal dunes from October to March. Light passage noted in April and September (exceptionally in August). More likely in remote cultivations and oases than Isabelline Wheatear. Call, a soft whistle, often heard in winter. – WV/pm

Finsch's Wheatear *Oenanthe finschii*

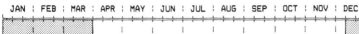

JAN	FEB	MAR	APR	MAY	JUN	JUL	AUG	SEP	OCT	NOV	DEC

Very rare winter visitor. A handful of records mid December to March, and mostly from sites near the Gulf coast. Usually disperses locally in winter from its central Asian upland breeding areas, including the mountains of western and northern Iran, to lower areas nearby. Generally scarce in Arabia. – wv

Red-tailed Wheatear *Oenanthe xanthoprymna* — Plate 15

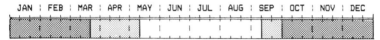

JAN	FEB	MAR	APR	MAY	JUN	JUL	AUG	SEP	OCT	NOV	DEC

Quite common winter visitor from October to mid March, when it occurs widely over broken hillsides, wadis and acacia plains, often in same habitat as resident Hume's Wheatear. May be found away from the mountains on passage from March, sometimes to early May. Recorded offshore in September. Pale-throated, and generally duller race *O. x. chrysopygia* occurs. – WV/pm

Eastern Pied Wheatear *Oenanthe picata* — Plate 15

JAN	FEB	MAR	APR	MAY	JUN	JUL	AUG	SEP	OCT	NOV	DEC

Scarce winter visitor (and possible passage migrant), September to March (one reported in April). Favoured habitat includes boulder-strewn gravel plains, semi-desert scrub and other open country. Most field observers confirm occurrence of sub-species *O. p. picata*, which is likely to be confused with Hume's Wheatear. Not recognised in Eastern Arabia until 1987, and a number of former reports are now being reconsidered. – wv/(pm)

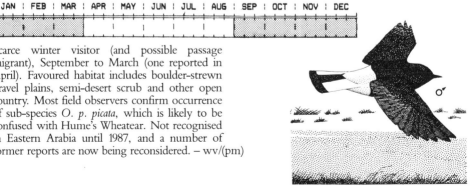

Mourning Wheatear *Oenanthe lugens*

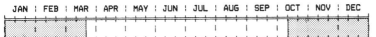

Scarce winter visitor from mid October to mid March, generally present only in stony areas of semi-desert, gravel plains, foothills and rocky gorges. Reports away from the mountains are often misidentified Pied Wheatear, though yellow-orange vent colouring is usually diagnostic. – wv

Hooded Wheatear *Oenanthe monacha*

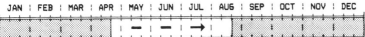

Status unclear, but probably scarce winter visitor and localised resident. Most recorded late August to mid April in rocky wadis, quarries, ravines and stony slopes. Many reported in mountainous areas around Ras al Khaimah, Hatta and Al Ain often in adjacent Omani territory. At least two pairs observed May and June 1990 on Jebel Hafit, probably nesting nearby. – wv/rb?

Hume's Wheatear *Oenanthe alboniger*   Plate 15

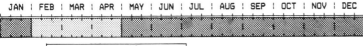

Hume's Wheatear

This common breeding resident is confined almost entirely to the foothills, stony slopes, wadis and ravines of the Hajar mountains, where it is familiar and well-known. Nests from January on remote rocky hillsides, laying up to five eggs in a rocky crevice. Scarce February to April until its young are fledged. Some dispersal (or migration) is reported between autumn and spring, when individuals have occurred away from their favoured mountain habitat, including on Das island (see Eastern Pied Wheatear). – RB/pm?

White-crowned Black Wheatear *Oenanthe leucopyqa*

Vagrant. One black-capped individual was reported on Das Island on 11th April 1987, (and one old record of a "Black Wheatear" at Ras al Khaimah could be this species). Other reports are unconfirmed or lack detail. Normally sedentary on the rocky hills of central and western Arabia. Recorded in Oman March to June, where status is unclear. – V

Rock Thrush *Monticola saxatilis*   Plate 16

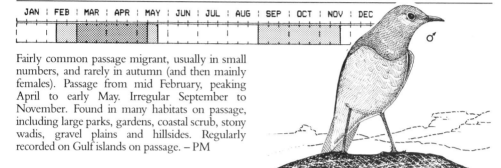

Fairly common passage migrant, usually in small numbers, and rarely in autumn (and then mainly females). Passage from mid February, peaking April to early May. Irregular September to November. Found in many habitats on passage, including large parks, gardens, coastal scrub, stony wadis, gravel plains and hillsides. Regularly recorded on Gulf islands on passage. – PM

Blue Rock Thrush *Monticola solitarius*

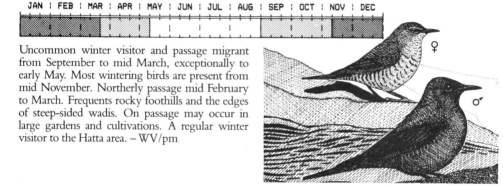

Uncommon winter visitor and passage migrant from September to mid March, exceptionally to early May. Most wintering birds are present from mid November. Northerly passage mid February to March. Frequents rocky foothills and the edges of steep-sided wadis. On passage may occur in large gardens and cultivations. A regular winter visitor to the Hatta area. – WV/pm

Ring Ouzel *Turdus torquatus*

Winter vagrant, with a handful of sightings reported November to January in a variety of locations including Das Island and the Emirates golf course. Generally rare in Arabia, its range normally restricted to northern temperate areas. Recorded February in Oman. – V

Blackbird *Turdus merula*

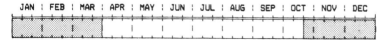

Scarce winter visitor late October to March. One found dead in Dubai in early May. Favoured habitat includes woodland, large gardens and shaded parks. Generally rare in Arabia. Nearest breeding areas are in central Iran. – wv

Eye-browed Thrush *Turdus obscurus*

Vagrant from north-east Asia. One at Asab oilfield 3/4 October 1988. – V

Note: – One at Masirah, Oman in late September 1974 - only other accepted Arabian record.

Black-throated Thrush *Turdus ruficollis*

JAN	FEB	MAR	APR	MAY	JUN	JUL	AUG	SEP	OCT	NOV	DEC

Scarce and irregular winter visitor from early November to mid March, occasionally October and April. More common some years than others. Favours man-made parkland and large gardens, although also found in cultivations and other sheltered areas. – wv/pm

Fieldfare *Turdus pilaris*

Winter vagrant, with only a handful of records in November and January in Dubai and Abu Dhabi (five reported together in Dubai's Saffa Park in mid January 1984). – V

Song Thrush *Turdus philomelos*

JAN	FEB	MAR	APR	MAY	JUN	JUL	AUG	SEP	OCT	NOV	DEC

The commonest migrant thrush. Regular winter visitor from November to March, (occasionally from late October to mid April). Favours large gardens, cultivations, palm groves, well-irrigated light woodland and parks, with shade and shelter. Often shy when its presence may only be betrayed by its distinctive alarm call from thick cover. Can be found in reasonable numbers in favoured habitat. – WV

Mistle Thrush *Turdus viscivorus*

JAN	FEB	MAR	APR	MAY	JUN	JUL	AUG	SEP	OCT	NOV	DEC

Rare winter visitor, less than a dozen records from mid November to March. In general, Arabia is outside its normal wintering range. Should not be confused with the more common and smaller Song Thrush. – V

Redwing *Turdus iliacus*

A winter vagrant. Up to three reported late November 1988 to January 1989 in Dubai and Abu Dhabi. All birds were in parkland habitat, and appeared wary. Generally rare throughout Arabian peninsula, where only records are from the Arabian Gulf coast. – V

Graceful Warbler *Prinia gracilis*   Plate 16

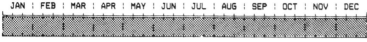

Very common breeding resident seen and heard throughout most of the year, wherever there are trees, shrubs and other suitable vegetation. Tiny and long-tailed, it is found in most parks, gardens and cultivations, its insistent trilling call is most distinctive. Adapts easily to new landscaped areas and soon colonisess them. Lays 3-5 eggs from March, in a cup nest at low level in a shrub or bush. Breeding activity noted in autumn aand winter some years. – RB

Scrub Warbler *Scotocerca inquieta*

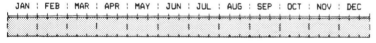

Uncommon breeding resident found only in mountain ravines, remote stony hillsides and steep rocky wadis, preferring low scrub and other sparse vegetation, where it can be most unobtrusive, unless call is heard. Its range extends from the foothills to summit level of some peaks. Nests from January in a low bush or tree. – RB
Note: Some field guides can mislead in suggesting similarities with *P. gracilis*. The two are actually quite different in song, habitat and head markings, and *S. inquieta* is practically unknown in gardens of the Gulf coast.

Grasshopper Warbler *Locustella naevia*

JAN	FEB	MAR	APR	MAY	JUN	JUL	AUG	SEP	OCT	NOV	DEC

An uncommon and localised spring passage migrant from mid March (irregularly from February) to April. Rarely in autumn, but some reported late July and August. Likely to be overlooked unless it is disturbed whilst skulking in uncut grass or undergrowth (when it will run in thick cover). Frequents damp thick vegetation, often in thickets near water, and overgrown pond edges. – pm

Savi's Warbler *Locustella luscinioides*

JAN	FEB	MAR	APR	MAY	JUN	JUL	AUG	SEP	OCT	NOV	DEC

Scarce passage migrant from early March to early May and less frequently in September. Most passage occurs further west, missing Eastern Arabia. Found in damp overgrown pond edges, ditches, reedbeds and tall grassland in irrigated areas. – pm

Moustached Warbler *Acrocephalus melanopogon*

Rare migrant, recorded in Dubai in December 1985 and mid May 1990. Small numbers breed in Saudi Arabia and Iran. Usually sedentary, but can be partly migratory and dispersive in winter. Favours low damp cover, near ponds and ditches. Care required to distinguish it from Sedge Warbler. – V

Sedge Warbler *Acrocephalus schoenobaenus*

JAN	FEB	MAR	APR	MAY	JUN	JUL	AUG	SEP	OCT	NOV	DEC

Fairly common, though localised passage migrant. Regular mid March to May, scarce mid September to mid October (exceptionally February, June and August). As other *Acrocephalus* warblers, it favours damp undergrowth near ponds, reeds, ditches and reservoirs, often feeding at water's edge. – pm

Marsh Warbler *Acrocephalus palustris*

JAN	FEB	MAR	APR	MAY	JUN	JUL	AUG	SEP	OCT	NOV	DEC

Common spring passage migrant from March, sometimes widespread and abundant in May with stragglers to early June. Small numbers August and September though passage poorly defined and much confused with Reed Warbler. Found wherever there are trees even at isolated oases and cultivations on passage. Generally favours irrigated parks, large gardens with thick cover and coastal scrub with scattered trees and bushes. – PM

Reed Warbler *Acrocephalus scirpaceus*

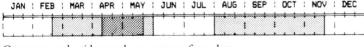

JAN	FEB	MAR	APR	MAY	JUN	JUL	AUG	SEP	OCT	NOV	DEC

Common and widespread on passage from late February, peak numbers occurring April to mid May. Extended autumn passage, when most records span August to November. Generally a little less common in spring than Marsh Warbler, though separation in the field is difficult. Favours damper areas, including reeds where available, though also likely in trees and bushes everywhere on migration. – PM

Clamorous Reed Warbler *Acrocephalus stentoreus*

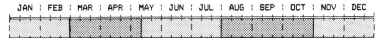

JAN	FEB	MAR	APR	MAY	JUN	JUL	AUG	SEP	OCT	NOV	DEC

 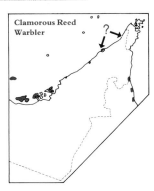

Common passage migrant, infrequent in winter. Small numbers resident in mangrove areas. Nests from April. Passage recorded in small numbers from March to May and dispersal noted from July, with passage August to October. Many in heavy moult in September. Migrants occur in damp overgrown areas around ponds, reedbeds, ditches and marshes. Distinguishing features include long dagger-like bill, and greyer plumage than Great Reed Warbler. – PM/wv/rb.

Great Reed Warbler *Acrocephalus arundinaceus*

JAN	FEB	MAR	APR	MAY	JUN	JUL	AUG	SEP	OCT	NOV	DEC

Irregular and localised passage migrant in small numbers mid August to October (to November some years), and less regularly mid March to mid May. Favours large parks or other areas with plenty of cover, not always near water. Generally in full (and distinctively rufous-brown) plumage in autumn, while Clamorous Reed Warbler is often in heavy moult. Insufficient separation between these two species has clouded many past records – pm

Icterine Warbler *Hippolais icterina*

Scarce passage migrant, and generally uncommon throughout the Arabian peninsula, its main passage probably occurring further west. Recorded late February to May, and August to September in trees and bushy areas. Winters in Africa, south of the Sahara. – pm

Olivaceous Warbler *Hippolais pallida*

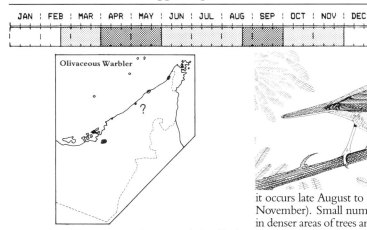

Fairly common passage migrant and localised breeding visitor. Passage mid March to May, and is particularly widespread from late April. In autumn it occurs late August to October (stragglers to late November). Small numbers nest from early April in denser areas of trees and bushes often near water. On passage found in dry acacia scrub, semi–desert with scattered trees, lightly wooded hillsides, parks and gardens. – PM/mb

Booted Warbler *Hippolais caligata*

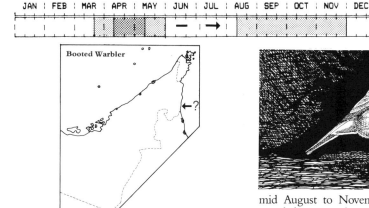

Regular passage migrant, rarely seen and often overlooked. May breed locally. Recorded regularly from March to May, with a less-obvious passage mid August to November. It occurs in lightly wooded areas and any other areas of trees and bushes, though it favours mangroves when nesting. Superficially similar to small *Phylloscopus* species, though its call is diagnostic. – pm/mb?

Upcher's Warbler *Hippolais languida*   Plate 16

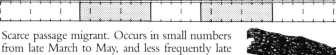

Scarce passage migrant. Occurs in small numbers from late March to May, and less frequently late July to September. Favours semi–desert scrub, gravel plains, hillsides with scattered trees and even town parks. Possible overlooked, or confused with Olivaceous Warbler. – pm

Note: Identification of this and other Hippolais warblers requires careful consideration.

Ménétries's Warbler *Sylvia mystacea*

Plate 16

| JAN | FEB | MAR | APR | MAY | JUN | JUL | AUG | SEP | OCT | NOV | DEC |

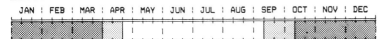

A common and widespread passage migrant, most common in early spring when peak passage is evident in March. Some remain until April. First autumn arrivals reported in late September and some overwinter locally. Recorded in parks, gardens and other areas of scattered trees and woodland, where it forages amongst cuttings, low thorn trees and scrub. Male distinctive, and in all plumages, tail waving is diagnostic. PM/wv

Note: The salmon-pink blush to underparts indicated in some field guides is not a notable feature on most birds occurring in the UAE.

Desert Warbler *Sylvia nana*

| JAN | FEB | MAR | APR | MAY | JUN | JUL | AUG | SEP | OCT | NOV | DEC |

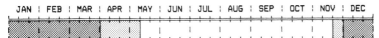

Regular winter visitor found in semi-desert scrub, coastal dunes, low bushes, gravel plains and other open country with minimal vegetation. Light passage from September with most overwintering birds present from mid October to March, a few remaining to April. Usually goes completely unnoticed, due to its small size and secretive habits. Rufous tail diagnostic. Often in presence of Red-tailed or Desert Wheatears, accompanying them and feeding in a bush beneath them. – WV

Orphean Warbler *Sylvia hortensis*

| JAN | FEB | MAR | APR | MAY | JUN | JUL | AUG | SEP | OCT | NOV | DEC |

Fairly common passage migrant and localised winter visitor, scarce before late November, and usually present until late March, exceptionally until early May. Some passage occurs from late February to late March. Favours light woodland, acacia groves and areas of semi-desert with scattered trees, although also likely in parks, gardens and cultivations. – pm/wv

Barred Warbler *Sylvia nisoria*

JAN	FEB	MAR	APR	MAY	JUN	JUL	AUG	SEP	OCT	NOV	DEC

Uncommon passage migrant, small numbers regularly in spring, particularly April and May. Less than a handful of records at other times including September to November (rare throughout Eastern Arabia in autumn). Found in denser areas of trees and patches of established woodland, including parks and large gardens with thick undergrowth. – pm

Lesser Whitethroat *Sylvia curruca*

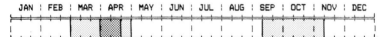

JAN	FEB	MAR	APR	MAY	JUN	JUL	AUG	SEP	OCT	NOV	DEC

Fairly common passage migrant in March and April. Irregular mid September to early November. Some in winter, but many confused with *S. minula* (formerly regarded as conspecific). Occurs in thick bushes and lightly wooded areas, in parks, larger gardens, oases, cultivations and acacia scrub. Usually located (and separated from other small *Sylvia* warblers) by its call – PM

Desert Lesser Whitethroat *Sylvia minula*

JAN	FEB	MAR	APR	MAY	JUN	JUL	AUG	SEP	OCT	NOV	DEC

Common and widespread winter visitor from late September to early April (stragglers reported to early May), favouring areas of scattered woodland, acacia gravel plains, ghaf trees groves, borders of cultivations, parks and large gardens. Sometimes in places with thick undergrowth, and usually located by its buzzing call. Formerly considered subspecies of *S. curruca,* with which it is often confused in the field. – WV

Hume's Lesser Whitethroat *Sylvia althaea*

Rare migrant. Recent sightings include one in early December 1988 near Hatta and one on gravel plain near Qarn Nazwa in early November 1989. Until recently the field characteristics of this form were little known, and it is still regarded as a sub-species of Lesser Whitethroat *S. curruca* by some. – V

Common Whitethroat *Sylvia communis*

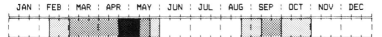

JAN	FEB	MAR	APR	MAY	JUN	JUL	AUG	SEP	OCT	NOV	DEC

Fairly common migrant with extensive spring passage from mid February (occasionally from January) to a peak late April to early May. Strays may occur to late May, even June. Less regular in autumn, when it is most common in September, though it has been reported over several autumn and early winter months. Frequents thickets, low acacia undergrowth, open woodland and ghaf tree groves. Also in gardens, parks and cultivations. – PM

Garden Warbler *Sylvia borin*

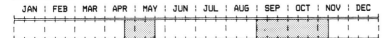

JAN	FEB	MAR	APR	MAY	JUN	JUL	AUG	SEP	OCT	NOV	DEC

Uncommon passage migrant, occurring late April to mid May, and September to early November, when it can be found in low trees or bushes, in parks, large gardens and cultivations often near water and regularly feeding on the ground. Overall uniformity and lack of field marks often assists identification. – pm

Blackcap *Sylvia atricapilla*

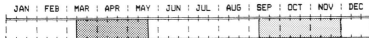

JAN	FEB	MAR	APR	MAY	JUN	JUL	AUG	SEP	OCT	NOV	DEC

Common and widespread spring migrant from mid March to mid May. Scarce in autumn, only a handful reported mid September to November. Found in damp thickets, and wooded undergrowth in parks, cultivations and well-established large gardens. Often present in small parties on passage. – PM

Yellow-browed Warbler *Phylloscopus inornatus*

JAN	FEB	MAR	APR	MAY	JUN	JUL	AUG	SEP	OCT	NOV	DEC

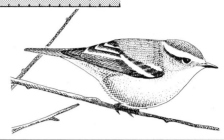

Scarce passage migrant and winter visitor, September to April. Regularly reported on Gulf islands and inland oilfields (probably attracted by the flares). Recorded in Dubai in March. Likely to favour bushes and trees on cultivations, acacia plains and bushy hillsides. – pm/wv

Bonelli's Warbler *Phylloscopus bonelli*

Vagrant. One exhausted bird found on Sir Abu Nu'air island in spring 1985. Other winter and spring reports in Dubai and Abu Dhabi under review. Main westerly migration routes normally miss Arabia. – V

Wood Warbler *Phylloscopus sybilatrix*

JAN	FEB	MAR	APR	MAY	JUN	JUL	AUG	SEP	OCT	NOV	DEC

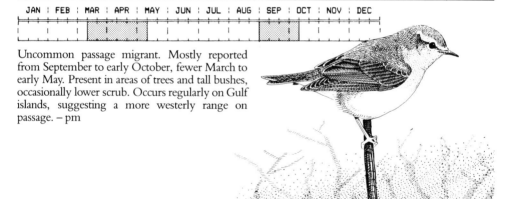

Uncommon passage migrant. Mostly reported from September to early October, fewer March to early May. Present in areas of trees and tall bushes, occasionally lower scrub. Occurs regularly on Gulf islands, suggesting a more westerly range on passage. – pm

Plain Leaf Warbler *Phylloscopus neglectus*

JAN	FEB	MAR	APR	MAY	JUN	JUL	AUG	SEP	OCT	NOV	DEC

Scarce winter visitor from mountainous breeding areas in Iran and its northern and eastern borders. Winter distribution in the Arabian region is uncertain, although small numbers occur in the Emirates in drier mountain wadis, on hillsides and associated gravel plains from mid October to March. Tiny size and harsh call are usually diagnostic. – wv

Plate 17

82 M. West

83 M. West

84 D. Robinson

85 Author

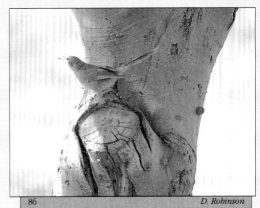

86 D. Robinson

82. Male Semi-collared Flycatcher *Ficedula semitorquata*, near Saffa Park pond, mid April 1982.   Text Page 153
83. Spotted Flycatcher *Muscicapa striata*, Dubai, September 1980.   " Page 154
84. Male Purple Sunbird *Nectarinia asiatica* (in glossy breeding plumage) feeding in *calotropis* bush,
    Ras Al Khaimah, April 1990.   " Page 155
85. House Crow *Corvus splendens*, Dubai old sewage treatment plant, May 1988.   " Page 158
86. Arabian Babbler *Turdoides squamiceps*, Ras al Khaimah, April 1990.   " Page 154

Plate 18

87   *D. Robinson*

89   *M. West*

88   *D. Robinson*

90   *Author*

87.   Isabelline Shrike *Lanius isabellinus,* Ras al Khaimah, early April 1990.   Text Page 156

88.   A female Isabelline Shrike near Al Ain, March 1990.

89.   Male Isabelline Shrike, Saffa Park.

90.   Male Isabelline Shrike, Dubai old sewage treatment plant, late April 1988.

Plate 19

91   *Author*

94   *J. A. D. Chapman*

92   *Author*

93   *Author*

95   *J. A. D. Chapman*

91.	Indian Silverbill *Euodice malabarica*, Saffa Park, late May 1989.	Text Page 162
92.	Red-backed Shrike *Lanius collurio*, Dubai, mid May 1989.	" Page 155
93.	Immature Rose-coloured Starling *Sturnus roseus*, Jebel Ali Hotel grounds, February 1988.	" Page 159
94.	Great Grey Shrike *Lanius excubitor* (of resident *aucheri* race). Note similarities with Lesser Grey Shrike.	" Page 156
95.	Northern Iranian *pallidirostris* race of Great Grey Shrike.	" Page 156

Plate 20

96   D. Robinson

97   D. Robinson

98   Author

99   Author

100   M. West

101   D. Robinson

96. Male Ortolan Bunting *Emberiza hortulana*, near Ras al Khaimah, early April 1989.   Text Page 165
97. House Bunting *Emberiza striolata*, Dhayah, north of Ras al Khaimah, late November 1989.   " Page 164
98. Male Yellow-throated Sparrow *Petronia xanthocollis*, Masafi hills, late May 1989.   " Page 162
99. Breeding male House Sparrow *Passer domesticus*, Jebel Ali Hotel, late April 1989.   " Page 160
100. Bank Mynah *Acridotheres ginginianus* in Dubai.   " Page 160
101. Common Mynah *Acridotheres tristis*, Abu Dhabi, winter 1989.   " Page 159

Chiffchaff *Phylloscopus collybita* Plate 16

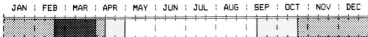

JAN	FEB	MAR	APR	MAY	JUN	JUL	AUG	SEP	OCT	NOV	DEC

Very common passage migrant and winter visitor from late October; first arrivals from mid September. Particularly widespread on spring passage when it appears in good numbers from late February to April. Sometimes confused with Willow Warbler which can be present from late March. Favours gardens, parks, cultivations and most areas of trees around habitation and landscaped areas in towns. Call is regularly heard in winter and spring. – wv/pm

Willow Warbler *Phylloscopus trochilus*

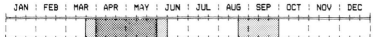

JAN	FEB	MAR	APR	MAY	JUN	JUL	AUG	SEP	OCT	NOV	DEC

Fairly common passage migrant, though not as widespread as Chiffchaff. Most common in April and May although small numbers do occur late March and early June. Has been reported singly at other times (though some likely confused with Chiffchaff). Scarce in autumn when most recorded late August and September. Present in cultivations, parks, large gardens and other areas of trees, though rarely in very dry areas. – PM

Blue-and-white Flycatcher *Muscicapa cyanomelana*

Vagrant from Eastern Asia. One recorded in foothills near Ras al Khaimah for several days in November 1980. – V

Semi-collared Flycatcher *Ficedula semitorquata* Plate 17

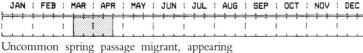

JAN	FEB	MAR	APR	MAY	JUN	JUL	AUG	SEP	OCT	NOV	DEC

Uncommon spring passage migrant, appearing from mid March to mid April (earlier than Spotted Flycatcher). There are less than a handful of autumn records, mostly females, in September and October. Occurs on the edge of wooded areas, in parks, large gardens and the edges of cultivations. Its origins include an area of wooded hills and mountains in the eastern Mediterranean and in the Armenian highlands. – pm

Note: Male remarkably similar to Pied Flycatcher *F. hypoleuca* and confusion may arise.

Pied Flycatcher *Ficedula hypoleuca*

Vagrant. Single males seen 31st March 1985 and 8th April 1986 in Dubai, and 6th April 1986 on Das Island – first known records for Eastern Arabia. Other reports suggest confusion with very similar Semi-collared Flycatcher. – V

154

Red-breasted Flycatcher *Ficedula parva*

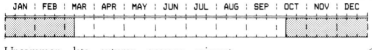

Uncommon late autumn passage migrant, occasionally wintering. Most occur from mid October to mid November, and has been reported in April and September. Very localised and irregular in winter, remaining in one location until March. Favours dense woodland in parks, large shaded gardens and cultivations and usually located by its 'ticking' call. – pm/wv

Spotted Flycatcher *Muscicapa striata*   Plate 17

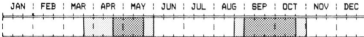

Common and regular passage migrant between Eurasian breeding grounds and Southern Africa. One of the first autumn migrants, and one of the last in spring. Present from late August to October (occasionally until December), and from late March to May. A few reports in other months. Found wherever there are trees or perches, in gardens, parks, cultivations, rubbish dumps, ghaf tree groves and other light woodland. – pm

Arabian Babbler *Turdoides squamiceps*   Plate 17

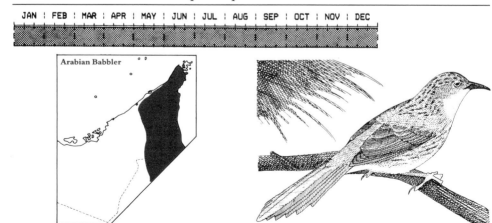

Breeding resident, confined mainly to northern and eastern areas of the country, where it is locally common in light woodland, sheltered wadis, gravel plains with scattered trees and scrub. Favours drier areas and particularly ghaf and acacia groves.

Regularly in small parties, it plays follow-my-leader from bush to bush, and can be curious and tame. Nests from February to mid summer high in a thorn tree or thick bush. – RB

Purple Sunbird *Nectarinia asiatica* Plate 17

JAN	FEB	MAR	APR	MAY	JUN	JUL	AUG	SEP	OCT	NOV	DEC

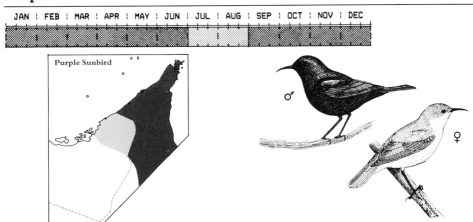

Very common breeding resident, widely present in parks and gardens, feeding on nectar and insects in flowering shrubs and bushes. It has colonised the gardens of the Arabian Gulf coast in recent years from its origins in the mountains where it also occurs in wadis, cultivations and on hillsides with scattered trees. Nests from early February, after the male's rather dull winter plumage moults to an irridescent purple. Numbers drop during July and August after breeding (when small insects are absent in the hot summer). Many are believed to disperse south, though these movements require further study. – RB

Golden Oriole *Oriolus oriolus*

JAN	FEB	MAR	APR	MAY	JUN	JUL	AUG	SEP	OCT	NOV	DEC

Fairly common passage migrant, though absent some years. Usually present from August to September, sometimes to mid October, and from late April to May, occasionally to June. Often in small parties, it is retiring and regularly overlooked, its yellow plumage often aiding its concealment in some foliage. Favours woodland of all kinds, including parks, large overgrown gardens and cultivations with high trees. – PM

Red-backed Shrike *Lanius collurio* Plate 19

JAN	FEB	MAR	APR	MAY	JUN	JUL	AUG	SEP	OCT	NOV	DEC

Fairly common spring migrant mid April to May. Irregular (though widespread some years) September to mid November. Favours thickets and light woodland in parks, edges of cultivations and large landscaped gardens with scattered trees. Autumn birds in winter/first-winter plumage may be confused with Isabelline Shrike. – PM

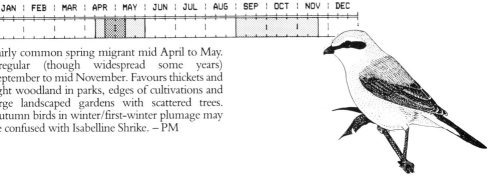

Isabelline Shrike *Lanius isabellinus* Plate 18

JAN	FEB	MAR	APR	MAY	JUN	JUL	AUG	SEP	OCT	NOV	DEC

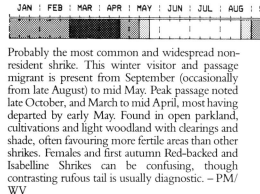
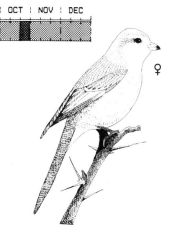

♀

Probably the most common and widespread non-resident shrike. This winter visitor and passage migrant is present from September (occasionally from late August) to mid May. Peak passage noted late October, and March to mid April, most having departed by early May. Found in open parkland, cultivations and light woodland with clearings and shade, often favouring more fertile areas than other shrikes. Females and first autumn Red-backed and Isabelline Shrikes can be confusing, though contrasting rufous tail is usually diagnostic. – PM/WV

Note: *L. i. phoenicuroides* and *L. i. isabellinus* commonly occur, the latter being more frequent on spring passage.

Bay-backed Shrike *Lanius vittatus*

Vagrant. Less than a handful of single birds recorded April, November and December mostly in cultivated areas. First recorded in April 1970 in Sharjah, and one remained two weeks at Digdaga, in November 1972. Also recorded in Oman. Generally sedentary in southern Iran and Pakistan. – V

Great Grey Shrike *Lanius excubitor* Plate 19

JAN	FEB	MAR	APR	MAY	JUN	JUL	AUG	SEP	OCT	NOV	DEC

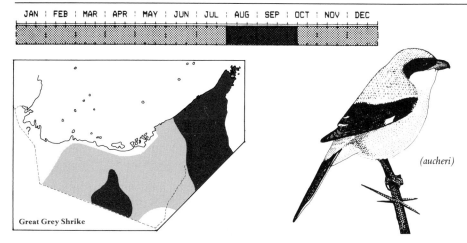

Great Grey Shrike

(aucheri)

Widespread resident and migrant throughout the region. Some winter locally. Generally common in autumn, when main passage recorded August to mid October. Less obvious passage in March and April. Favours semi-desert, open country, edges of cultivations, wadis, gravel plains and any areas with scattered trees and a prominent perch. Scarce late January to April when residents are nesting. It lays 2-6 eggs from January in an acacia tree or bush. Local race *L.e.aucheri* has an extended black mask and black bill, and confusion can occur with Lesser Grey Shrike. Northern Iranian race *L. e. pallidirostris* common on passage. – RB/PM/wv

Lesser Grey Shrike *Lanius minor*

JAN	FEB	MAR	APR	MAY	JUN	JUL	AUG	SEP	OCT	NOV	DEC

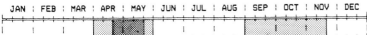

Uncommon passage migrant, most occurring April and May. Irregular in autumn September to mid November. Recorded in parkland and cultivations, where it favours scattered trees, bushes and thicket borders. Can be confused with resident race of Great Grey Shrike *L. excubitor aucheri*, which has a more extensive black mask. – pm

Woodchat Shrike *Lanius senator*

JAN	FEB	MAR	APR	MAY	JUN	JUL	AUG	SEP	OCT	NOV	DEC

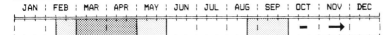

Common spring migrant, usually widespread though numbers can vary annually. It is one of the earliest passage migrants, occurring widely from February to April, peaking in March. Sometimes in January and May. Scarce and irregular in autumn, when it has been recorded late August to mid November. Frequents large gardens, irrigated landscaped parks and cultivations, although may turn up in a number of more remote areas, including wadis and plains. – PM

Masked Shrike *Lanius nubicus*

JAN	FEB	MAR	APR	MAY	JUN	JUL	AUG	SEP	OCT	NOV	DEC

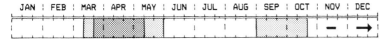

Uncommon spring passage migrant, most occurring mid March to late May. Irregular in autumn (less than a handful of records) from September to November, and two overwintered in Abu Dhabi 1988–89. Occurs in wooded scrub, large gardens, cultivations and open parkland, favouring a shaded perch. – pm

House Crow *Corvus splendens*

Plate 17

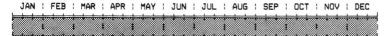

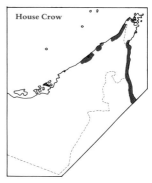

Abundant resident of East Coast towns, harbours and fishing villages where it is becoming a pest. On the Gulf coast most occur north of Ras al Khaimah. Small numbers are now colonising other Gulf coastal areas, including Dubai where it is locally common. Favours areas with tall trees, in parks, large gardens, especially palm groves and cultivations, though rarely far inland. Often mobs other birds, especially birds of prey, and can be quite inquisitive. Nests from April, and may colonise new areas in March when nest prospecting. – RB

Brown-necked Raven *Corvus ruficollis*

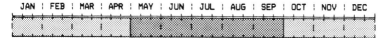

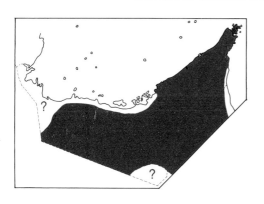

Fairly common resident, wide ranging and catholic in taste of habitat. Found in barren desert, semi-desert, gravel plains, mountains, foothills and coastal dunes, and generally away from towns and coasts. Often seen soaring, and assembles in large scavenging parties in summer and autumn. Occasionally preys on other medium-sized birds. Nests from January to April in a solitary bush or tree, with eggs reported in March. – RB

Starling *Sturnus vulgaris*

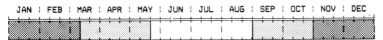

JAN	FEB	MAR	APR	MAY	JUN	JUL	AUG	SEP	OCT	NOV	DEC

Common and localised winter visitor, numbers varying from year to year. Occasionally occurs as early as September, though most arrive in November. Main departure early March, with small numbers remaining to mid May. Seen in foraging flocks, often of fifty or more birds, and sometimes several hundred, in parks, gardens, cultivations and sewage works. – WV

Rose-coloured Starlings

Rose-coloured Starling *Sturnus roseus*   Plate 19

JAN	FEB	MAR	APR	MAY	JUN	JUL	AUG	SEP	OCT	NOV	DEC

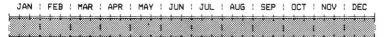

Regular though elusive autumn passage migrant. First arrivals in August are usually small parties of juveniles, staying until September (occasionally to October) and some may overwinter. Strong east-west migrant and individuals can occur in all months. Favours parks, large wooded gardens and cultivations, usually feeding on the ground. Retreats to high perches (perhaps in a casuarina or eucalyptus tree) and is generally shy. – pm

Common Mynah *Acridotheres tristis*   Plate 20

JAN	FEB	MAR	APR	MAY	JUN	JUL	AUG	SEP	OCT	NOV	DEC

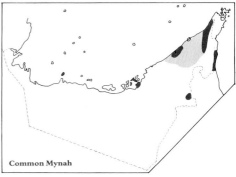

Common Mynah

A widely introduced locally abundant resident, breeding ferally and spreading. Adaptable, and well established in and around the parks and gardens of the coastal towns and some inland areas. Particularly common in Dubai and Abu Dhabi. A confident, noisy and gregarious bird, it is commonly seen on road verges and roundabouts. Nests in holes, including broken lamp-posts from February to July, though nesting period appears to vary annually. – RB/E

Bank Mynah *Acridotheres ginginianus* — Plate 20

| JAN | FEB | MAR | APR | MAY | JUN | JUL | AUG | SEP | OCT | NOV | DEC |

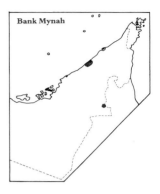

Scarce and localised breeding species, all probably introduced. A dispersive and opportunist breeder. It nests in colonies in exposed sand banks from April, with juveniles present July and August.

Favours open country with scattered trees, or sewage outflows with reeds and other cover. Only recorded in Abu Dhabi, Dubai and Al Ain where small colonies are expanding. – rb/E

House Sparrow *Passer domesticus* — Plate 20

| JAN | FEB | MAR | APR | MAY | JUN | JUL | AUG | SEP | OCT | NOV | DEC |

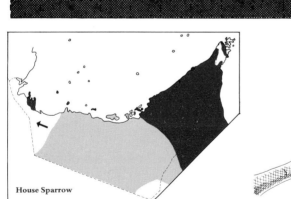

Abundant and well-known breeding resident, whose numbers appear to be increasing dramatically in some areas. Occurs in towns and villages, even in more remote regions, often moving in large flocks from one favoured feeding place to another. Nests from January to August (peaks March and April), laying up to 6 eggs. The pale sub-species *P. d. indicus* occurs. – RB

Spanish Sparrow *Passer hispaniolensis*

JAN	FEB	MAR	APR	MAY	JUN	JUL	AUG	SEP	OCT	NOV	DEC

Very scarce and irregular winter visitor from late November to early March, when large flocks have occurred. Generally found in similar habitat to House Sparrow, though it may also be found in more remote uninhabited areas. – wv

Tree Sparrow *Passer montanus*

Vagrant. Nearest breeding areas are northern Iran and Turkey, where it is believed to be sedentary. Almost unknown in Arabia save for sightings 7th March and 9th November 1984 in Dubai, and two separate sightings on Das Island on 8th and 23rd September 1986. – V

Pale Rock Sparrow *Petronia brachydactyla*

JAN	FEB	MAR	APR	MAY	JUN	JUL	AUG	SEP	OCT	NOV	DEC

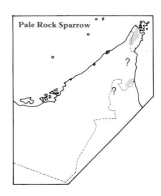

Pale Rock Sparrow

Irregular spring passage migrant and localised summer breeding visitor. Fairly common March to April, occasionally earlier. Scarce September to October. Can occur in open country on passage (including salt scrub), though appears to favour stony hillsides and wadis near mountain cultivations when nesting (and following wet winters). Nesting in UAE first suspected in Wadi Qawr area, near Hatta, where fledgelings were found in August 1988. – PM/cb

Yellow-throated Sparrow *Petronia xanthocollis* — Plate 20

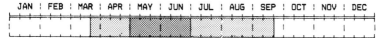

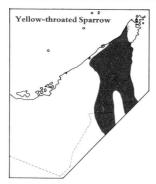

Common breeding summer visitor, present from March to September (individuals on passage some years to November). Nests May to July in trees in semi-desert, gravel plains, wadis and foothills, and particularly in ghaf and acacia groves, and in arid sand dune areas. Can be overlooked in House Sparrow flocks, and best located by its distinctive call. – MB/pm

Note: Juveniles and plain-throated females can be confused with Pale Rock Sparrow *Petronia brachydactyla*.

Indian Silverbill *Euodice malabarica* — Plate 19

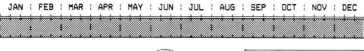

A fairly common resident. Found in small, restless and apparently nomadic flocks in semi-desert, wadis, gravel plains with scattered acacia, and around farms and cultivations even in remote desert and mountain areas. Its range is extending into the Western Region, where it is found in the remote cultivations of the Liwa oases. Eggs recorded January and February, though nesting has been recorded up to July. A popular cage-bird, and some populations in Dubai and other Gulf coastal towns originate from escapes. – RB/E

Chaffinch *Fringilla coelebs*

Vagrant. One female wintered early January to mid February 1987, then one male occurred on 22 March of same year on Das Island. No confirmed reports yet on UAE mainland. Has wintered in adjacent Gulf states. – V

Brambling *Fringilla montifringilla*

Rare winter visitor, recorded only a handful of times since first report in November 1977 in Abu Dhabi. Reported from November to February, sometimes in small groups and might be found in damp open areas, including fields, parkland and sewage works, with nearby cover. – V

Goldfinch *Carduelis carduelis*

Vagrant. Two together in Abu Dhabi in January 1987. Nearest breeding grounds include eastern Iran where 'Grey-headed' race is resident. Also kept as a cage-bird. – V

Siskin *Carduelis spinus*

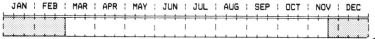

JAN	FEB	MAR	APR	MAY	JUN	JUL	AUG	SEP	OCT	NOV	DEC

Irregular winter visitor, sometimes in flocks from late November to February. Most from early December. Favoured habitat includes parkland, gardens and cultivations with conifer and *casuarina* trees. – wv

Linnet *Carduelis cannabina*

Vagrant, recorded less than a handful of occasions in a variety of locations in November and February. Favours scrub, open ground, including cut hay fields and coastal marshes. – V

Trumpeter Finch *Bucanetes githagineus*

JAN	FEB	MAR	APR	MAY	JUN	JUL	AUG	SEP	OCT	NOV	DEC

Status unclear in the Emirates (and most of Eastern Arabia). Most reported late October to March in foothills and adjacent plains, stony wadis and mountain slopes. May nest locally, including Jebel Hafit. Probably overlooked due to small size and shy habits, and more information needed. – wv?/rb?

164

Common Rosefinch *Carpodacus erythrinus*

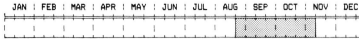

JAN	FEB	MAR	APR	MAY	JUN	JUL	AUG	SEP	OCT	NOV	DEC

Uncommon spring passage migrant from late August to early November. Rarely in other months, although there are isolated records December to March. Found in damper areas of parkland, wooded scrub and mountain wadis with thick vegetation. Apart from adult males, identification of this species can be a challenge, particularly in autumn. – pm

Yellowhammer *Emberiza citrinella*

Vagrant. One on Das Island 17th March 1987 only acceptable record for the UAE (and Arabia). Other reports show confusion with Yellow-breasted Bunting, and with Finn's Baya Weaver (Yellow Weaver) a popular aviary species. – V

House Bunting *Emberiza striolata*   Plate 20

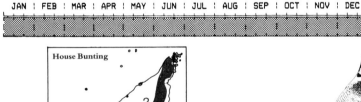

JAN	FEB	MAR	APR	MAY	JUN	JUL	AUG	SEP	OCT	NOV	DEC

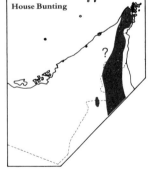

Common and localised breeding resident of the mountains. Favours wadis, acacia plains and stony hillsides up to quite high altitudes. Numbers wander to adjacent plains, foraging in flocks in winter, sometimes with Black-crowned Finch Lark. Active at dawn when flocks head for feeding areas. Found in small parties feeding unobtrusively on the ground often near water. Nests amongst rocks from March to early May, laying three eggs. – RB

Note: very similar to Rock Bunting *E. cia* which is not recorded on the Arabian peninsula (resident in Iran).

Rustic Bunting *Emberiza rustica*

Vagrant. A handful of records December to February in Dubai and on some Gulf islands. First recorded December 1985. Traditional wintering grounds lie within China. – V

Cinereous Bunting *Emberiza cineracea*

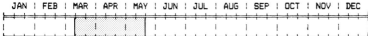

JAN	FEB	MAR	APR	MAY	JUN	JUL	AUG	SEP	OCT	NOV	DEC

Rare spring passage migrant. Less than a handful of accepted sightings mid March to May in a variety of locations throughout the Emirates. Will favour semi-desert and wadis on passage, and is possibly under-recorded. – pm

Ortolan Bunting *Emberiza hortulana*   Plate 20

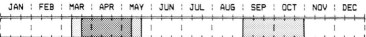

JAN	FEB	MAR	APR	MAY	JUN	JUL	AUG	SEP	OCT	NOV	DEC

Probably the most regular migrant bunting particularly in spring, when likely to be found from late March to mid May. Autumn passage occurs September to late October, occasionally to November. Sometimes overlooked, it feeds quietly on open ground or grass, in parks, large gardens, desert scrub and cultivations. Winters in southern Arabia and in Africa just south of the Sahara. – PM

Little Bunting *Emberiza pusilla*

Vagrant. Single birds recorded on Gulf islands late October to November, and up to three stayed for a week on Das Island in early November 1987.

Dynamic migrant breeding in surbarctic zone, and wintering in South-east Asia. – V

Yellow-breasted Bunting *Emberiza aureola*

Vagrant. One reported in December 1980 in the mountains near Ras al Khaimah. Winter birds likely to be confused with Yellowhammer. Favours dry open country. – V

Note: Reported in neighbouring areas of Musandam and Northern Oman August to November.

Reed Bunting *Emberiza schoeniclus*

Vagrant. Two in Abu Dhabi late November 1978. Reports of single birds in Dubai mid February 1982 and late March 1980 lack detail. Usually favours damp marshy areas. – V

Black-headed Bunting *Emberiza melanocephala*

| JAN | FEB | MAR | APR | MAY | JUN | JUL | AUG | SEP | OCT | NOV | DEC |

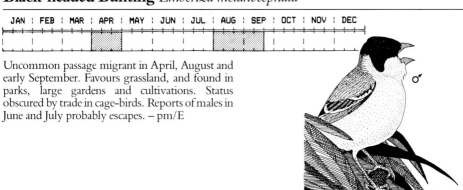

Uncommon passage migrant in April, August and early September. Favours grassland, and found in parks, large gardens and cultivations. Status obscured by trade in cage-birds. Reports of males in June and July probably escapes. – pm/E

♂

Corn Bunting *Miliaria calandra*

| JAN | FEB | MAR | APR | MAY | JUN | JUL | AUG | SEP | OCT | NOV | DEC |

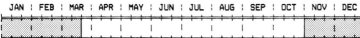

Uncommon and irregular winter visitor, mostly November to mid March, and usually in small numbers, although 200 overwintered in Abu Dhabi 1977-78. Found in cultivations, irrigated parkland and large gardens with trees and bushes, and may exceptionally occur in drier scrub areas and lightly wooded hillsides. – wv

...STOP PRESS....STOP PRESS....STOP PRESS....STOP PRESS....STOP PRESS....STOP PRESS....STOP PRESS.

There is still much to be learnt about the UAE's birds. New species are being regularly reported, and others are having their status revised. The following updates were received too late for inclusion in the main species text:

Grey-headed Kingfisher *Halcyon leucocephala*

One was reported at Assab oilfield in the western desert region from 14-17th June 1990. This species is a common summer breeding visitor to the mountains of south-east Arabia (including Dhofar, Oman).

European Roller *Coracias garrulus*

Several were found in Digdaga, Ras al Khaimah late May to July 1990, where suitable nesting habitat of irrigated fields and scattered tall trees is now well established. One juvenile was reported in early July, a first breeding record for the UAE.

Species not on Main List

Lesser Frigatebird *Fregata ariel*

A report referring to one or more Lesser Frigatebirds landing exhausted on board a ship off the southern Arabian Gulf coast in March 1955 (*Sea Swallow* 19:78) lacks substantiating detail. Generally of unlikely occurrence in the UAE (particularly the Arabian Gulf), although there have been accepted frigatebird reports off the Musandam peninsula and Northern Oman coast in May 1972 and June 1982.

Intermediate Egret *Egretta intermedia*

Not yet recorded in the UAE. Known reports appear to be mistakenly identified *E. a. modesta*, a race of Great White Egret which is noticeably smaller than the nominate race, though still somewhat larger than Intermediate Egret. One was recorded at Khasab, Musandam in late November 1988.

Sacred Ibis *Threskiornis aethiopicus*

Two free-flying individuals appeared at Khor Dubai in October 1982. Their origin was never established, although this species is often kept in open aviaries at Al Ain Zoo and some private collections. Vagrancy from resident breeding areas (nearest southern Iraq) is possible and further evidence of this is needed.

Egyptian Goose *Alopochen aegyptiacus*

Several hundred introduced and breeding on Sir Bani Yas Island, and smaller numbers reported breeding around Abu Dhabi lagoon areas 1989, with chicks reported in May. Generally popular in private collections, many free-flying.

Rüppell's Vulture *Gyps rueppellii*

A number of reports, though most believed to refer to Lappet- faced Vulture *Torgos tracheliotus* whose field identification continues to confuse observers (and which was little known in the region prior to 1982). From its African range it has been recorded only in the extreme south of the Arabian peninsula.

Black Vulture *Aegypius monachus*

Status uncertain. Many reported sightings probably refer to Lappet-faced Vulture. Might occur as a scarce winter visitor to the foothills and mountains from Asian breeding grounds, though fully acceptable field description still awaited. Considered vagrant in Oman following the discovery of a dead bird on Masirah.

Rough-legged Buzzard *Buteo lagopus*

Status under review. A number of reports over the years, including individuals in October and late November in the south of the country. Not generally likely to occur in Arabia, although evidence appears to be mounting for its future inclusion in the UAE list. Can be mistaken for Long-legged Buzzard.

Black Francolin *Francolinus francolinus*

Introduced population (possibly 100's of birds) on Sir Bani Yas Island recorded September 1989, and one or two reported in Abu Dhabi from May 1977 to September 1979, probably released from private collection. No wild breeding population (nearest Iran) of this normally sedentary species reported in Arabia.

Little Crake *Porzana parva*

Several reports, many confused with Baillon's Crake. Generally very scarce in Arabia, though possibly occurs on passage. Acceptable description not seen.

Great Stone Plover *Esacus recurvirostris*

Not yet reported. Breeds directly across the Straits of Hormuz on the coastline of southern Iran and is considered a prospective vagrant to UAE, particularly to the East Coast. One was recorded in Oman late January to early February 1989.

Golden Plover *Pluvialis apricaria*

Status obscured due to its similarity to the more common Pacific Golden Plover *P. fulva* with which it is often confused. Reported August to May on or near coasts, though most records very uncertain. In general the Gulf is outside its normal short-range migration which seldom brings it nearer than the southern shores of the Caspian Sea.

Spur-winged Plover *Hoplopterus spinosus*

One Abu Dhabi, mid January 1988, under review. Near East populations often sedentary, though dispersal is regularly reported in winter throughout the Arabian peninsula. Single birds occurred in Northern Oman in November 1985 and December 1986.

Long-toed Stint *Calidris subminuta*

No substantiated records for UAE. Reported August to May in Oman, and has occurred in Iran and Saudi Arabia. Considered a prospective vagrant and may be overlooked.

Asiatic Dowitcher *Limnodromus semipalmatus*

Unlikely to occur. Reports of its vagrancy in the UAE (Hollom, Porter *et al* 1988) believed to be based on flocks seen in Sharjah in March 1945. These records are under review to rule out Bar-tailed Godwit. (Smaller race *L. 1. lapponica* is common).

Slender-billed Curlew
Numenius tenuirostris

Possible vagrant from western Siberia. Reported in Abu Dhabi and on Qarnayn Island, though reports lack substantiating detail. One of the world's scarcest waders, whose migratory routes are generally unknown. Similar in size to Whimbrel, and in other ways to eastern race Curlew *N. a. orientalis*. Preferred habitat includes shallow inland waters and tidal mudflats.

Oman reports suggest some may reach eastern Arabia regularly. Recorded in Northern Oman April-May 1976, and in January 1990 at Barr al Hikman, opposite Masirah Island.

Far-eastern Curlew
Numenius madagascariensis

There are several unsubstantiated reports of its occurrence, and reports in other Gulf states are under review. Some may be of eastern race Curlew *N. a. orientalis,* which regularly occurs. Might be overlooked, unless dark rump noted in flight. Has been recorded in Iran.

South Polar Skua
Catharacta maccormicki

Juvenile strays likely to occur in Arabian Sea, though none yet reported from UAE waters. Disperses from Antarctic breeding areas February to April. Generally hard to tell apart from Great Skua (page 104).

Black Tern *Chlidonias niger*

Several reports of birds in non-breeding plumage. No satisfactory description seen, and no breeding adults recorded which would rule out commoner 'marsh' terns. Generally rare throughout Arabia.

Common Noddy *Anous stolidus*

Not yet recorded, though it has probably passed unobserved through UAE territorial waters. Uncommon summer visitor to Gulf of Oman, including Musandam (Gallagher and Woodcock 1980).

Black-bellied Sandgrouse
Pterocles orientalus

Several reported sightings in Dubai area. Probably fragments of introduced populations and not considered to be a native resident. Some reports show confusion with Chestnut-bellied Sandgrouse.

Woodpigeon *Columba palumbus*

Not yet reported in UAE, though considered a prospective stray to East Coast cultivations. Local breeding resident in Jebel Akhdar area, Northern Oman, and has wandered in winter to interior and Batinah coastal plain.

Dunn's Lark *Eremalauda dunni*

Not recorded in the UAE. However, as with a number of lark species its movements on the Arabian peninsula are not well understood. It breeds in Saudi Arabia and Southern Oman, and is nomadic outside the breeding season. It is likely to be overlooked.

Bar-tailed Desert Lark
Ammomanes cincturus

One dead bird was found at Jebel Ali in March 1971. Nearest breeding areas of this normally sedentary species lie within Saudi Arabia and Southern Oman. Often associated with Dunn's Lark in ground feeding parties. Nested on Bahrain in 1987.

Blyth's Pipit *Anthus godlewski*

Not known in Arabia, though several reports are currently under review. This eastern form of Tawny Pipit is likely to be confused with Richard's Pipit *A. novaeseelandiae* and some first-winter Tawny Pipits *A. campestris*. Known breeding range includes Mongolia and China.

Red-whiskered Bulbul
Pycnonotus jocosus

An introduced species, originating from the Indian sub-continent. Has occurred in Dubai suburbs, where a pair nested in a garden in May 1985 though few sightings since. Escapes may be quick to colonise, though no evidence of feral population forming as has occured with White-cheeked and Red-vented Bulbuls.

Pied Stonechat *Saxicola caprata*

Resident and partial migrant breeding from Iran to the Far East. Not recorded in the Emirates, although one male of race *S. c. bicolor* was found in Khasab, Musandam in April 1983. Skin in British Museum (Natural History).

Blyth's Reed Warbler
Acrocephalus dumetorum

Not recorded in the UAE. Possibly overlooked, though undoubtedly rare in Eastern Arabia. Report in March from Northern Oman under review. One Bahrain record.

Green Warbler *Phylloscopus nitidus*

No acceptable records known. Potential spring and autumn vagrant. Recorded as scarce in Oman August to November, and has occurred in Bahrain and northern Saudi Arabia in spring. Breeds in northern Iran and Armenia, wintering in southern India.

Greenish Warbler
Phylloscopus trochiloides
No records yet for the UAE. Unsure reports in late November and late March not accepted. Recorded as vagrant in Southern Oman late August, October and early November, having overflown Gulf region to occur there.

Arctic Warbler *Phylloscopus borealis*
Not recorded in the UAE. Vagrant in Oman and eastern Saudi Arabia, and strays could occur in the Emirates.

Long-tailed (Black-headed) Shrike
Lanius schach
One reported mid March 1988 on Abu Dhabi Island, and currently under consideration.
Single birds recorded in southern Oman in February 1983 and 1984.

Pied Mynah *Sturnus contra*
First reported regularly in Dubai, Abu Dhabi and Sharjah in spring and summer 1989. Breeding and nesting activity noted, though no other details known. Surprisingly widespread, and assumed introduced, though total numbers reported in spring 1990 were less than ten.

Brahminy Mynah *Sturnus pagodarum*
Several reports in the Dubai area since 1985, probably released birds, with breeding activity noted May 1987 and 1988. Favours open parkland, large gardens and light woodland.

Rüppell's Weaver *Ploceus galbula*
A few reported in parks and suburban gardens, particularly in Dubai. Records in spring and summer assumed to be of released cage-birds by people departing for annual leave. Occasional reports of pairs nest-building in Dubai, though further details not known. A common breeding resident in southern Arabia, and a feral population breeds in Riyadh (and probably in other towns in Arabia).

Note: Other introduced weavers likely to occur include Masked Weaver *P. intermedius*, Streaked Weaver *P. manyar*, Finn's Baya Weaver *P. megarhynchus* and Black-breasted Weaver *P. benghalensis*.

Red Avadavat *Amandava amandava*
A popular cage-bird, and many escape or are introduced. Very small finch-like birds (male is bright red), likely to favour gardens, reeds and damp areas. Sometimes found in small flocks. A pair built a nest in a Sharjah garden in June 1988, raising two young. Origins include Pakistan and India.

Red-headed Bunting *Emberiza bruniceps*
A report of this species occurring as a vagrant in the UAE (Hollom, Porter *et al* 1988) is believed to be based on a July sighting of a male in the garden suburbs of Dubai. The release of large numbers of cage-birds in the summer by owners when they leave is a common phenomenon, and this species (always male) is imported from Pakistan for sale on the local market. As a result this species has been removed from the UAE checklist.

SPECIES ALSO RECORDED IN UAE BUT ESCAPED FROM CAPTIVITY (OR DELIBERATELY RELEASED).

Marabou Stork
Red-billed Teal
Hawaiian Goose
Fulvous Whistling Duck
Dark-chanting Goshawk
Gyrfalcon
Crowned Crane
Diamond Dove
Barbary Dove
Cockatiel
Alexandrine Parakeet (reported nesting)
Blossom-headed Parakeet
Moustached Parakeet
Peach-faced Lovebird
Fischer's Lovebird
Budgerigar
Pekin Robin
Black Drongo (two in Dubai, December 1986 to January 1987)
Indian Tree Pie
Jungle Mynah
Crested Mynah (numbers in Dubai January 1984 to 1986; smaller numbers, Abu Dhabi)
Spreo Starling
Chestnut Munia
Scaly-breasted Munia
Waxbill
Java Sparrow
Finn's Baya Weaver
Streaked Weaver
Masked Weaver
Black-breasted Weaver
Red Bishop
Red-headed Bunting

References

Ali, S. and Dillon, S. 1983 *A Pictorial Guide to the Birds of the Indian Subcontinent.* Bombay Natural History Society, New Delhi.

Bahrain Natural History Group Newsletter. A monthly journal. BNHS, P.O. Box 20336, Manama, Bahrain.

Birding World. A monthly journal. Stonerunner, Coast Road, Cley-next-the-Sea, Holt, Norfolk, UK.

Bulletin, published 4-monthly by the Emirates Natural History Group (Abu Dhabi), P.O. Box 2380, Abu Dhabi, UAE.

British Birds. A monthly journal. Fountains, Park Lane, Blunham, Bedfordshire, UK

Bruun, B. and Singer, A. 1971 *The Hamlyn Guide to the Birds of Britain and Europe.* Hamlyn, Feltham.

Cramp, S. and Simmons, K.E.L. (eds.) 1977-88 *The Birds of the Western Palaearctic* Vols. 1-5. Oxford University Press.

Dubai Natural History Group. *Gazelle,* published monthly. DNHG, P.O. Box 9234, Dubai, UAE.

Emirates Natural History Group Newsletter. Published monthly. ENHG (Abu Dhabi), P.O. Box 2380, Abu Dhabi, UAE.

Ferguson-Lees, I.J., Willis, I. and Sharrock, J.T.R. 1983 *The Shell Guide to the Birds of Britain and Ireland.* Michael Joseph, London.

Fitter, R., Parslow, J. and Heinzel, H. 1972 *The Birds of Britain and Europe with North Africa and the Middle East.* Collins, London.

Gallagher, M. (Editor) *Oman Bird News* 1986 – Published quarterly on behalf of the Oman Bird Records Committee. Oman Natural History Museum, P.O. Box 668, Muscat, Sultanate of Oman.

Gallagher, M. and Woodcock, M.W. 1980 *The Birds of Oman.* Quartet Books, London.

Harrison, Colin 1982 *An Atlas of the Birds of the Western Palaearctic.* Collins, London.

Harrison, P. 1985 *Seabirds: an identification guide.* Croom Helm, Beckenham.

Harrison, P. 1987 *Seabirds of the World: a photographic guide.* Christopher Helm, Bromley.

Jennings, M.C. 1981 *Birds of the Arabian Gulf.* George Allen & Unwin, London.

Jennings, M.C. 1981 *The Birds of Saudi Arabia: a checklist.* Published by the author. Whittlesford, Cambridge.

Journal of Oman Studies Special Reports. (1975-) Published by the Ministry of Information and Culture, Sultanate of Oman.

King, B., Woodcock, M. and Dickinson, E.C. 1975 *A Field Guide to the Birds of South East Asia.* Collins, London.

Madge, S. and Burn, H. 1988 *Wildfowl: an identification guide to the ducks, geese and swans of the world.* Christopher Helm, Bromley.

Marchant, J., Prater, T. and Hayman, P. 1986 *Shorebirds: an identification guide to the waders of the world.* Croom Helm, Beckenham.

Mead, Chris 1983 *Bird Migration.* Country Life Books, Rushden, England.

Nightingale, T. and Overy, M. (eds.) 1987 *Wildlife in Bahrain.* Bahrain Natural History Society, P.O. Box 20336, Bahrain.

Ornithological Society of the Middle East. *Sandgrouse* , published annually.

Phoenix. A newsletter compiled and distributed by M.C. Jennings for contributers to *The Atlas of the Breeding Birds of Arabia* in prep. M.C. Jennings, Moonraker Cottage, 1 Eastcourt, Burbage, Marlborough, Wiltshire.

Porter, R.F., Willis, I., Christensen, S. and Nielsen, B.P. 1981 *Flight Identification of European Raptors.* Poyser, Calton.

Richardson, C. *Emirates Bird Report* 1987 - (formerly Dubai Bird Report). Compiled and published quarterly. Distributed by the Dubai Natural History Group.

Rogers, T.D. 1988 *A new list of the Birds of Masirah Island.* The Oman Bird Records Committee, P.O. Box 246, Muscat, Sultanate of Oman.

Sea Swallow. The Annual Report of the Royal Naval Bird Watching Society.

Vinicombe, Keith. 1989 *The Macmillan field guide to bird identification.* Macmillan, London.

Voous, K.H. 1973, 1977 *List of recent Holarctic bird species* (reprinted, and amended from *Ibis*)

Warr, F.E. *A list of the Birds of the United Arab Emirates.* Printouts prepared for private circulation. Compiled by Mrs. F.E. Warr.

Western, R.A. 1989 *The Flora of the United Arab Emirates– an introduction.* Published by the United Arab Emirates University.

Woodcock, M. 1980 *Collins handguide to the Birds of the Indian Sub-continent.* Collins, London.

INDEX OF ENGLISH NAMES

The figures in bold type refer to the photo Plates, and those in standard type to the main descriptive text, and introduced species.

INDEX OF SCIENTIFIC NAMES

The figures in bold type refer to the photo Plates, and those in standard type to the species' descriptive text.

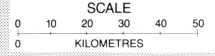

N

ARABIAN

GULF

SHAR
Khor Kha
DUBAI

Saffa Park

Zabe

Jebel Ali

Emirates Go
Course

UNITED

ARAB

EMIRATES

ABU
DHABI

Al Wathba